Table of Contents

INTRODUCTION

YOUR COMMITMENT TO THIS BIBLE STUDY

A house is built by wisdom, and it is established by understanding;
by knowledge the rooms are filled with every precious and beautiful treasure.

—

Proverbs 24:3-4 Holman CSB

You're about to begin a six-week course about building a stronger marriage. Congratulations—your willingness to add new tools to your marital toolkit shows that you're committed to your spouse, to your family, and to God.

During the next few weeks, you'll be asked to read, to study, to pray, to learn, and to change some old habits. To derive the greatest benefits from this course, you'll need to set aside time each day to study the ideas on these pages and to think carefully about the ways that you can apply these concepts as you build an ever-deepening relationship with your mate.

Do you sincerely want to become a better marriage partner? With God's help, you can do it. It may not be easy to build a stronger marriage, and it may not be quick, but it's certainly possible. What's required is a sincere desire to learn, a willingness to trust God's Word, and a readiness to take these lessons seriously. When you do, you'll learn that while building a stronger marriage isn't always painless, it's always worth the effort. And you'll learn that there are absolutely no challenges—including the inevitable challenges of marriage—that you and your mate, working together and with God, can't handle.

Our Group

Meeting Time & Day:

Start Date:

Group Leader's Name(s):

Phone Number:

Thing to Remember About Them:

Group Member's Name(s):

Phone Number:

Thing to Remember About Them:

Group Member's Name(s):

Phone Number:

Thing to Remember About Them:

Group Member's Name(s):

Phone Number:

Thing to Remember About Them:

Group Member's Name(s):

Phone Number:

Thing to Remember About Them:

Group Member's Name(s):

Phone Number:

Thing to Remember About Them:

Group Member's Name(s):

Phone Number:

Thing to Remember About Them:

Group Member's Name(s):

Phone Number:

Thing to Remember About Them:

Group Member's Name(s):

Phone Number:

Thing to Remember About Them:

Group Member's Name(s):

Phone Number:

Thing to Remember About Them:

Group Member's Name(s):

Phone Number:

Thing to Remember About Them:

Week 1

THE BIBLICAL FOUNDATIONS OF MARRIAGE

Unless the Lord builds a house, its builders labor over it in vain; unless the Lord watches over a city, the watchman stays alert in vain.

—

Psalm 127:1 Holman CSB

God's Word has much to say about your marriage, about your spouse, and about you. And if you're wise, you'll pay careful attention to what the Creator says.

In the first week of this course, we will examine what God's Word says about wives, husbands, and marriage. We'll discuss the differences between men and women. And we'll consider ways that thoughtful spouses can learn to celebrate their differences and, by doing so, strengthen the ties that bind.

DAY 1: A BETTER MARRIAGE IS POSSIBLE, BUT SOME PAIN IS INEVITABLE

DAY 2: CULTURAL CONFUSION ABOUT THE ROLES OF MEN AND WOMEN

DAY 3: DIFFERENT ORIGINS AND DIFFERENT PURPOSES

DAY 4: DIFFERENT CONSEQUENCES, DIFFERENT BODIES

DAY 5: MARRIAGE IS . . .

Day 1

A BETTER MARRIAGE IS POSSIBLE, BUT SOME PAIN IS INEVITABLE

Choose for yourselves this day whom you will serve . . . .
But as for me and my house, we will serve the Lord.

—

Joshua 24:15 NKJV

THOUGHT FOR THE DAY

If you and your spouse want to build a stronger marriage, you can most certainly do it. What's required is a willingness to learn, a willingness to work, a willingness to change, and a willingness to make God your partner.

Do you sincerely desire to build a better marriage? If so, the good news is this: A stronger marriage is possible. The Bible teaches us that all things are possible through God (Luke 1:37, Matthew 17:20). So if you and your mate genuinely desire a better marriage, you most certainly can have it if you're willing to work with God. But here's a word of warning: as you and your spouse make changes to your relationship— by working carefully and prayerfully on your marriage—some pain is inevitable. And that's okay because the pain you experience today has the potential to bring great gain (and greater intimacy) tomorrow.

Perhaps you had little or no training in preparation for your marriage. If so, you're a member of a very large club. Too few couples have meaningful prenuptial counseling. Or perhaps you're laboring under the misconception that because you have conflict, you and your mate are in the minority. In truth, almost all married couples experience conflict—yet if that conflict is addressed properly, it serves as a way for couples to grow closer, not farther apart.

So if your marriage isn't perfect, don't despair. No marriage is perfect—every marriage is three steps forward and two steps back. Because you and your spouse, like all members of the human race, are sinners living

in a fallen world, you will inevitably hurt each other from time to time. But God can use your pain as a way of binding you and your mate closer together, and that's precisely what He'll do . . . if you let Him.

A MARRIAGE TIP

Don't expect a pain-free marriage. There is no intimacy apart from pain.

Christian maturity is not the absence of problems; it's about what you do with those problems. And a good Christian marriage is not about the absence of conflict; it's about what you do with that conflict . . . and how you choose to resolve it.

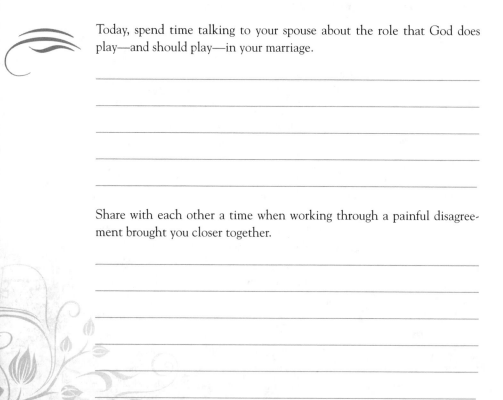

Today, spend time talking to your spouse about the role that God does play—and should play—in your marriage.

_____

_____

_____

_____

_____

Share with each other a time when working through a painful disagreement brought you closer together.

_____

_____

_____

_____

_____

QUESTIONS TO CONSIDER

1. Even though many of the Jewish tribes were compromising and defecting from the Lord, to what did Joshua commit for himself and his family?

_____

2. Marriage is not pain-free, nor should it be. After all, in marriage, there is no_____ without pain.

3. In marriage progress is _____ and _____ is inevitable.

Pain Does Not Equal the End of a Marriage: Into every marriage, a little pain must fall—or perhaps a lot of pain. But the presence of pain doesn't mean the end of the marriage. Far from it! The pain may actually be a path to greater intimacy. So don't ignore the pain in your marriage; work through it as a way of gaining greater intimacy with your mate.

COMMITMENT FIRST!
The best marriages are built upon an unwavering commitment to God and an unwavering commitment to one's spouse. So, if you're totally committed, congratulations; if you're not, you're building your marriage (and your life) on a very shaky foundation.

GREAT THOUGHTS ABOUT MARRIAGE

Marriage is God's idea. He "crafted" it. If your marriage is broken, take it to Him. The Creator who made it in the first place can make it work again.
—*Anne Graham Lotz*

On the pleasant days of marriage, gaze across at your groom and conclude he is worth it. On the difficult days of marriage, gaze up at your Groom and conclude He's worth it.
—*Beth Moore*

On the lines below, jot down your own goals for this course. And then, during the next six weeks, refer back to this page often as a way of gauging your progress.

_____

_____

_____

_____

_____

_____

_____

_____

_____

_____

_____

_____

_____

_____

_____

_____

_____

_____

_____

_____

_____

_____

_____

_____

> Being committed
> to one's mate is not
> a matter of demanding rights,
> but a matter of releasing rights.
>
> —
>
> *Charles Swindoll*

Day 2

CULTURAL CONFUSION ABOUT THE ROLES OF MEN AND WOMEN

God created man in His own image, in the image of God He created him;
male and female He created them.

—

Genesis 1:27 NASB

THOUGHT FOR THE DAY

Society stresses the sameness of the sexes, but God's Word recognizes—
and celebrates—the differences between men and women.

Psalm 127 teaches us that unless God builds a house, its builders labor in vain. And the same can be said for marriages: If we want to experience God's blessings, we must let Him rule over our homes and our marriages. But here in the real world, plenty of Christian couples don't. Oh, there's no shortage of lip service that's paid to God, but when it comes down to the realities of everyday married life, far too many couples simply don't concern themselves too much with the Creator's marriage manual which, by the way, is contained inside the 66 books of the Holy Bible. And that's not too surprising because modern culture seems to ignore God with vigor.

Gloria Steinem, the famous American feminist, once claimed, "Differences between men and women are a result of cultural expectations and sexist parenting." But just because Miss Steinem said it doesn't make it so. In truth, men and women are (of course) very different. Nonetheless, modern society stresses the sameness of the sexes and popular culture creates confusion between husbands and wives. Even homosexual partnerships are endorsed as a legitimate form of marriage. And Satan rejoices.

God's Word makes it perfectly clear that men and women have different origins and different purposes. And what do these differences mean to married couples? Simply this: If husbands and wives seek to experience God's blessings upon their families and their marriages, they must cut

through society's intellectual clutter by returning, without hesitation or apology, to God's Holy Word . . . and to God's plan for marriage.

Have you and your mate been victimized by the muddled ideas of pop psychologists who would have you believe that there exists only superficial differences between men and women (and, by extension, between husbands and wives)? If so, it's time to pay more attention to God's Word and less attention to society's propaganda.

Men are different from women . . . and thank goodness for those differences!

CHOOSE THE RIGHT ARCHITECT

If you are going to build a marriage made in heaven, why not follow His Divine Design? God has given us His plans in the Bible. You've got to study them, and build accordingly.

QUESTIONS TO CONSIDER

1. God's wisdom is perfect wisdom. In 2 Timothy 3:16-17 (Holman CSB), we are a taught that, "All Scripture is inspired by God and is profitable for _____, for _____, for _____, for training in _____, so that the man of God may be complete, equipped for every good work."

True / False

☐ ☐ 2. Society has a system of beliefs, a system that sometimes differs dramatically from God's Word. As a result, confusion from the culture is rampant.

☐ ☐ 3. Popular culture often stresses equality, even sameness, between the sexes. The Bible, on the other hand, acknowledges the differences between the sexes.

CELEBRATE THE DIFFERENCES

Society minimizes the differences between men and women; thoughtful Christians celebrate those differences. On the lines below, jot down some of the ways that you and your spouse differ from each other.

_____

_____

_____

_____

_____

_____

_____

_____

_____

_____

_____

_____

_____

_____

_____

_____

_____

_____

_____

_____

_____

Day 3

DIFFERENT ORIGINS AND DIFFERENT PURPOSES

The Lord God took the man and placed him in the garden of Eden to work it and watch over it . . . . Then the Lord God said, "It is not good for the man to be alone. I will make a helper who is like him." . . . Then the Lord God made the rib He had taken from the man into a woman and brought her to the man.

—

Genesis 2:15, 18, 22 Holman CSB

THOUGHT FOR THE DAY

Man was formed from the ground for the ground and is therefore work-oriented. Woman was formed from a man, for a man; she is, therefore, relationally oriented.

Ninety-nine percent of Christians don't know that Adam was created before the Garden of Eden, but that's precisely how it happened. The Bible teaches us that Adam was formed from the dust before the garden was created (not after). Thus Adam was created in an unbounded place: no fences, no borders; thus, he thrives on independence. And because he was made from the ground, Adam was oriented to the ground. Therefore, Adam was work-oriented. And so are the vast majority of men. Most men are task-oriented, work-oriented, and achievement-oriented; they want to accomplish things, big things. They are created by God to toil and to accomplish.

The woman Eve was formed from a man, for a man. She was created after the Garden of Eden was planted; thus, she was created in a bounded place, so she longed for security . . . and women still do. They focus on their connection to a place (the home). And so it is that women long to make their homes a comfortable, safe nest.

So, while a man longs to extend his reach and accomplish his responsibilities, a woman will tend to focus more upon the security of home life and the sanctuary of strong relationships.

Different Origins

Man was formed from dust, with no boundaries, and with a need to work the soil from which he came.

Woman was formed from man, for man. She is relationally oriented, and she yearns for security.

Different Purposes

Man was brought to a garden (Genesis 2:16); he was formed from the ground for the ground.

Woman was brought to a man, not to a garden. In a sense, she was "twice made," by God, from man. And since woman was formed from a man, her primary focus is on relationships.

Both a good marriage and a bad marriage have moments of struggle, but in a healthy relationship, the husband and wife search for answers and areas of agreement because they love each other.

—

James Dobson

Focus on the Bible

Thoughtful Christian couples understand that the Bible is unlike any other book. It is a priceless gift from our Creator, a tool that God intends for us to use in every aspect of our lives, including marriage. In short, God's Word is the ultimate guide for life and the ultimate marriage manual.

Corrie ten Boom advised, "Don't worry about what you do not understand of the Bible. Worry about what you do understand and do not live by." And that's solid advice for Christian couples whether they've been married six days or sixty years.

Would you like to energize your marriage and your life? Then open your Bible and read it with a focused mind and an open heart. And remember: God has given you the Bible for the purpose of knowing His promises, His power, His commandments, His love, and His Son. As you and your spouse study God's teachings and apply them to your lives, you both will learn to live by the Word that shall never pass away with a focused mind and an open heart (try Genesis 1, 2, and 3).

QUESTIONS TO CONSIDER

True / False

☐ ☐   1. The Bible teaches that the differences between men and women are few, and that those differences don't really matter very much.

☐ ☐   2. Because man was created before the Garden of Eden, he was, in his original state, unbounded.

☐ ☐   3. Woman, like man, was also made unbounded.

DIFFERING VIEWPOINTS

How do you and your spouse see the world differently? How do these differences impact your marriage? Do you complement each other or compete with each other?

_____

_____

_____

_____

_____

_____

_____

_____

_____

_____

_____

_____

_____

_____

_____

Day 4

DIFFERENT CONSEQUENCES, DIFFERENT BODIES

*He said to the woman: I will intensify your labor pains; you will bear children
in anguish. Your desire will be for your husband, yet he will dominate you.
And He said to Adam, "Because you listened to your wife's voice
and ate from the tree about which I commanded you, 'Do not eat from it':
The ground is cursed because of you. You will eat from it
by means of painful labor all the days of your life."*

—

Genesis 3:16-17 Holman CSB

THOUGHT FOR THE DAY

As a result of original sin, man will have difficulty accomplishing his
work. And woman will have difficulty in building relationships and
bringing her children to maturity.

When man and woman rebelled against God in the Garden of
Eden, they were both punished, but in different ways. As a
consequence of his rebellion, man was to experience "painful
labor" throughout his life. And when you stop to think about it, things
haven't changed too much since those ancient times. Despite the relative
affluence of the 21st century, men still experience difficulty accomplishing
their work. In a time of relative plenty, most men in the world still live
from paycheck to paycheck (if they earn a paycheck at all). And despite
countless scientific and economic breakthroughs, most men around the
globe still struggle to meet the needs of their families.

Women, on the other hand, face a different set of consequences. The
pain of childbirth is an obvious result of original sin (Genesis 3:16), but
it doesn't stop there; women also endure emotional pains. How? Women
experience difficulty in building trusting relationships (far too many
women find it almost impossible to trust their husbands completely.). And
women also experience great emotional pain in bringing their children to
maturity. Finally, Genesis 3:16 teaches us that women will be troubled by

issues of control within the marriage. Wives, out of their insecurity, will try to control their husbands. Husbands, out of their insecurity, will try to dominate, rather than be godly (servant) leaders.

So in summary, we see that as a result of original sin:

1. Man has difficulty with his work;
2. Woman has difficulty:
    A. Building relationships;
    B. Bringing children to maturity;
    C. With issues of control inside the marriage.

A MARRIAGE TIP

Face facts: You and your mate are constructed differently. You see the world differently. You have different responsibilities, different tendencies, and different bodies. Try your best to understand those differences . . . and celebrate them.

Different Bodies Tell the Story: Both men and women are made in the image of God, equal in humanity but different in design. And if you don't believe men are different from women, simply look at their respective bodies. Men have more upper body strength, while women are softer and smoother (designed to nurture).

Modern science has revealed that male and female brains have important differences (not surprisingly, women access feelings more quickly than men).

So think of it like this: Men are designed to sweat while women are designed to sculpt relationships. And thankfully, men and women are intended to complement each other—it's God's way.

Wives beware: You may try to control your husband because of a lack of trust, but your efforts will result in even more insecurity.

Husbands beware: You may focus too intently on work and not enough on your family.

QUESTIONS TO CONSIDER

1. Because woman was created from man, one of her greatest needs is . . .

   A. Meaningful work

   B. Money

   C. Security

   D. Freedom from all restraints.

2. The consequence of original sin for man is that he will have difficulties in his _____. The consequences for woman are that she will have pain in childbirth and difficulties in her close personal _____.

True / False

☐ ☐   3. Man and woman are equal in humanity but different in design.

NOTES

PRAISING THE DIFFERENCES

On the lines below, list some of the best things you like about differences between you and your spouse.

_____

_____

_____

_____

_____

_____

_____

_____

_____

_____

_____

_____

_____

_____

_____

_____

_____

_____

_____

_____

_____

_____

_____

_____

_____

_____

_____

Day 5

MARRIAGE IS . . .

Now these three remain: faith, hope, and love.
But the greatest of these is love.

—

1 Corinthians 13:13 Holman CSB

THOUGHT FOR THE DAY

Marriage is permanent; parenting is temporary.

A healthy marriage is a lifelong exercise in love, fidelity, trust, understanding, forgiveness, caring, sharing, and encouragement. It requires empathy, tenderness, patience, and perseverance. It is the union of two adults, both of whom are willing to compromise and, when appropriate, to apologize. It requires heaping helpings of common sense, common courtesy, and uncommon caring. A healthy marriage is a joy to behold, an even greater joy to experience . . . and a blessing forever.

The loving relationship between a husband and wife may require the couple to travel together through the dark valleys of anger, disappointment, and sorrow, but even on those darkest days, the couple can remain steadfast . . . if they choose to follow God.

Oswald Chambers, the author of the Christian classic devotional text, *My Utmost For His Highest*, advised, "Never support an experience which does not have God as its source, and faith in God as its result." These words serve as a powerful reminder that, as Christians, we are called to walk with God and to obey His commandments. But as we make our daily journey with God, we travel through a world that presents us with countless temptations to stray far from His path. So we must be watchful, we must be thoughtful, and we must be obedient to God.

When we behave ourselves as obedient servants, we honor the Father and the Son. When we live righteously and according to God's commandments, we build better marriages and better lives. When we obey God, He blesses us in ways that we cannot fully understand. So, as this day unfolds, take every step of your journey with God as your traveling companion. Study His Holy Word. Follow His commandments. Support

only those activities that further God's kingdom and your spiritual growth. Be an example of righteous living to your neighbors, to your children, and to your spouse. And make certain that you keep God where He belongs: at the center of all your relationships, including your marriage.

A MARRIAGE TIP

Remember: Marriage is blessed by God, ordained by God, and designed by God to reveal Christ's love for the church.

COOPERATION, NOT COMPETITION

Have you and your mate learned the art of cooperation? If so, you have learned the wisdom of "give and take," not the foolishness of "me first." Cooperation is the art of compromising on many little things while keeping your eye on one big thing: your marriage.

In cooperative marriages, both husbands and wives recognize (and learn to celebrate) their differences. But, whenever couples fail to cooperate with each other, they sow the seeds of dissatisfaction, frustration, and competition within their marriage. In such cases, marriage partners may find themselves engaged in an unwitting "contest" to receive their "fair share" from the relationship, or competing with each other in a power struggle for control. These types of struggles inevitably create far more problems than they solve.

If you're like most of us, you're probably a little bit headstrong: you probably want most things done in a fashion resembling the popular song "My Way." But, if you are observant, you will notice that those people who always insist upon "my way or the highway" usually end up with the latter.

A better strategy for all concerned (including you) is to abandon the search for "my way" and search instead for "our way." The best marriages are those in which both partners learn how to "give and take" . . . with both partners trying to give a little more than they take.

A Few More Things to Remember

1. Marriage is not competing with your spouse. Marriage is complementing your spouse.
2. If you want a healthy marriage, you should accept and celebrate the differences between you and your mate.
3. Wise couples don't try to change one another; they learn to appreciate one another.

Questions to Consider

1. It is important for couples to _____, and not to _____ with one another.

True / False

☐ ☐ 2. Marriage is designed by God, ordained by God, and designed by God to reveal Christ's love for the Church.

☐ ☐ 3. 1 Corinthians 13:13 teaches the importance of faith, hope, and love, but the most important is faith.

We've grown to be one soul—
two parts; our lives are so intertwined
that when some passion stirs your heart,
I feel the quake in mine.

—

Gloria Gaither

MORE ACCEPTANCE AND GREATER APPRECIATION

What do I need to do to better accept and appreciate my spouse? In what ways do we complement each other?

_____

_____

_____

_____

_____

_____

_____

_____

_____

_____

_____

_____

_____

_____

_____

_____

_____

_____

_____

A marital relationship that
endures and becomes more
fulfilling for both the husband
and the wife is no accident.
Only hard work makes
a marriage more fulfilling.

—

Gary Smalley

Week 2

MAN'S RELATIONSHIP TO GOD

In the beginning was the Word; and the Word was with God,
and the Word was God. He was with God in the beginning.
All things were created through Him, and apart from Him
not one thing was created that has been created.

—

John 1:1-3 Holman CSB

This week, we'll examine how the first man was related to God. And we'll ask you to think about the way that you and your spouse are currently relating to the Creator.

The best way to live—for married folks and singles alike—is to be directly, sincerely, completely, and permanently "hard-wired" into God. This week, we'll invite you and your mate to improve your connection with the ultimate Source of energy, wisdom, and love.

//

DAY 1: WHEN SIN ENTERED THE GARDEN: THE LOSS
OF SIGNIFICANCE AND SECURITY

DAY 2; TWO PROBLEMS OF MARRIAGE: DEMANDS
AND DISILLUSIONMENT

DAY 3: DIFFERENTIATION

DAY 4: SHARING GOD'S LOVE WITH THE RIGHT KIND
OF CIRCUITRY

DAY 5: LIGHTENING UP ON YOUR MATE,
TIGHTENING UP WITH GOD

Day 1

WHEN SIN ENTERED THE GARDEN: THE LOSS OF SIGNIFICANCE AND SECURITY

It is written: There is no one righteous, not even one.

—

Romans 3:10 Holman CSB

THOUGHT FOR THE DAY

There are certain needs that our mate can meet and certain needs that only God can meet. If we are wise, we learn the difference.

In the beginning, God gave man the responsibility to rule (Genesis 1:26-28). Man was also given the responsibility of sharing a relationship with God (a vertical relationship) and with man's surroundings (horizontal relationships). Because of his relationship with God, man had significance and security. Thus from creation, man had two attributes: 1. Significance (from the responsibility God gave to man) and 2. Security (from the relationship God had with man).

Then came the entrance of sin and, with it, the negative consequences of sin. Fear entered into man's relationship with God (Genesis 3:10), and insecurity entered into the woman's relationship with man (Genesis 3:10). In describing Adam and Eve, Dr. Larry Crabb observed,

> "Security and significance were attributes or qualities already resident within their personalities, so they never gave them a second thought. When sin entered their innocence and broke their relationship with God, what formerly were attributes now became needs."

As a result of original sin, security—security in man's relationship to man and man's relationship to God—became insecurity. And, man's responsibility to rule—by which he had previously gained significance—became a potential source of insignificance.

THE NEEDS GOD MEETS

There are certain needs that our spouses can meet and certain needs that only God can meet. When we expect our spouses to quench the thirsts that only God can quench, we'll be disappointed.

In the 4th chapter of John, Jesus spoke to (but did not condemn) a woman who had been trying (unsuccessfully) to find love in all the wrong places. She was a woman thirsty for love, and Jesus did not condemn her thirst. Christ promised her that God offers a "living water" to those who are willing to worship Him in spirit and in truth.

Will you worship God in spirit and in truth? And will you let Him quench your spiritual thirst today and every day? Or do you expect your spouse to meet all your needs, including the needs that only God can meet? The answer is up to you. And so are the consequences.

A MARRIAGE TIP

Only as we find our deepest sense of significance and security in our relationship with Jesus will we be able to come to marriage with an ability to give rather than just take.

Jesus: The Source of Living Water, Real Unfailing Love: Jesus gets below the surface in our lives as individuals to help us see where we are employing wrong strategies to meet our needs for security (love) and significance. Women will often give their bodies hoping to be loved. This was the case for the woman at the well. She kept looking to men to fill her need for love. Jesus presented Himself as the One and Only One who could satisfy her deepest needs. He wanted her to understand that where she had been looking was not effective. No man had made her feel really loved, and now she had even given up on the institution of marriage and was just living with a man. She responded to the understanding Jesus gave her and the offer of real life satisfaction in Him.

NON-CONDEMNING EXPOSURE

Jesus does not expose our sin to condemn us, but rather to show that our wrong strategies for love or significance do not work.

QUESTIONS TO CONSIDER

1. Would you describe Jesus as a counselor who dealt with issues above the surface or below the surface?

_____

_____

2. If Jesus got below the surface with you, what might be revealed about your strategies to meet your deepest needs?

_____

_____

_____

_____

3. Did exposure move the woman closer to Jesus or farther away?

_____

_____

4. Do you believe that Jesus was condemning the woman at the well when He told her to go and get her husband (when He knew that she had no husband and was living with a man who was not her husband)? (John 4:16-18)

_____

_____

_____

ANOTHER MARRIAGE TIP

Today, spend time talking to your spouse about the role that God does play—and should play—in your marriage. And while you're at it, talk about the needs that your spouse can meet and the needs that only God can meet.

Today, too many folks are looking for love in the wrong places and from the wrong people. List some of the places—and some of the activities— that Christian couples are wise to avoid.

_____

_____

_____

_____

_____

_____

How might the pursuit of position or the acquisition of possessions be a way people look for significance?

_____

_____

_____

_____

_____

_____

_____

If you expect your mate to do the things that only God can do, you'll be terribly disappointed every time.

Day 2

TWO PROBLEMS OF MARRIAGE: DEMANDS AND DISILLUSIONMENT

It is better to take refuge in the Lord than to trust in man.

—

Psalm 118:8 Holman CSB

THOUGHT FOR THE DAY

If you expect your spouse to meet your deepest personal needs, you'll be disappointed and disillusioned. If you look to God for your deepest needs, you'll be satisfied and blessed.

Every married couple faces two potential problems: "demandingness" (nagging) and disillusionment. Demandingness occurs when we expect someone or something other than God to meet our deepest needs. Disillusionment occurs when we realize that the particular someone or something cannot meet our deepest needs. Oswald Chambers observed,

> "The refusal to be disillusioned is the cause of much of the suffering in human life. It works in this way—if we love a human being and do not love God, we demand of him every perfection and every rectitude, and when we do not get it, we become cruel and vindictive; we are demanding of a human being that which he or she cannot give. There is only One Being Who can satisfy the last aching abyss of the human heart, and that is the Lord Jesus Christ."

If we are to grow spiritually and emotionally, it is important that all of us—husbands and wives alike—become disillusioned with the limitations of our mates. Refusal to become disillusioned only leads to more nagging and continued hostility. But once we realize that our spouses can do some things for us but not everything, then we are finally freed from our unrealistic expectations . . . and we are free to become truly intimate with God.

A MARRIAGE TIP

We must learn to view disillusionment as a doorway to a deeper intimacy with God. Why? Because it is only after we become disillusioned with our mate that we may seek greater intimacy with Him.

QUESTIONS TO CONSIDER

1. What would a refusal to be disillusioned or disappointed with our mate look like?

_____

_____

_____

_____

_____

2. Becoming disillusioned with our mate can be a good thing. Why?

_____

_____

_____

_____

_____

True / False

☐ ☐ 3. All couples face disillusionment from time to time, but it is important for the marriage partners to see that disillusionment as an opportunity for deeper intimacy with God.

One of the biggest problems in marriage is that we keep on trying to get our mate to meet our needs rather than looking to God. How does this hurt your marriage? What are you asking your mate to do that is really God's responsibility?

_____

_____

_____

_____

_____

_____

_____

_____

_____

_____

_____

_____

_____

_____

_____

_____

_____

_____

_____

_____

_____

_____

_____

> Love is most often found in
> the home—in the presence
> of a caring and considerate
> mate who nurtures love daily.
>
> —
>
> *Zig Ziglar*

Day 3

DIFFERENTIATION

Come, everyone who is thirsty, come to the waters;
and you without money, come, buy, and eat!
Come, buy wine and milk without money and without cost!

—

Isaiah 55:1 Holman CSB

THOUGHT FOR THE DAY

Learn to see yourself as dynamically attached to God, not to your spouse. After all, only God can meet your deepest needs.

What is differentiation in marriage? It is the ability to see yourself as a unique individual who is dynamically hooked up to the Lord, not to your mate. When you learn (and put into practice) the principle of differentiation, you and your mate will finally be free to become mature adults living in intimate connection with God. And that divine connection will revolutionize your marriage.

Couples who understand the principle of differentiation are aware of an important, unalterable truth: It is only when husbands and wives link themselves directly to the Creator that they free themselves from the chains of negativity and hostility—it is only then that they are free to enjoy each other completely and without reservation.

How can you and your mate move toward differentiation? Here are three steps:

1. Recognize your tendency to control or "fix" and label that tendency a sin (because that's precisely what it is).
2. Repent from your need to "repair" your mate, and turn instead to the Lord. Ask God to meet your needs first (Psalm 46:1-2), and then confidently ask Him to meet your spouse's needs (Philippians 1:6).
3. Reenter your relationship with a new, non-controlling attitude and a renewed commitment to love your mate as he or she actually is, complete with his or her imperfections.

The results of differentiation are profoundly helpful:

1. Your mate will feel accepted.
2. You and your spouse will be free to share together.
3. You and your mate will enjoy each other more because neither is assuming undue responsibility for the other.

So, as you go about the important work of building a better marriage, remember this: It is only by connecting fully to God that you can become really connected to your mate.

A MARRIAGE TIP

Admit to God your attempts to control your mate. Learn to let your mate be in a mess. Then, ask God to meet your needs first, and then ask God to meet your mate's needs.

Peace with God. Peace with self. Peace with others. Do you possess that kind of peace? Have you found the genuine peace that can be yours when you're directly linked to Jesus Christ, or are you still complaining about—and rushing after—the illusion of "peace and happiness" that the world promises but cannot deliver? The words of John 14:27 remind us that Jesus offers us peace, not as the world gives, but as He alone gives. Our challenge is to accept Christ's peace into our hearts and then, as best we can, to share His peace with our loved ones and our neighbors.

Today, as a gift to yourself, to your spouse, to your family, and to your friends, claim the inner peace that is your spiritual birthright: the peace of Jesus Christ. It is offered freely; it has been paid for in full; it is yours for the asking. So ask. And then share.

Since the Christian's Point of Reference is the Bible,
it's a happy couple who look there for guidance.

—

Ruth Bell Graham

QUESTIONS TO CONSIDER

1. The best way to move toward differentiation is to recognize our tendency to control our spouses and to acknowledge that it is _____.

True / False

☐ ☐   2. In a healthy marriage between two Christians, it's important that both husbands and wives see their mates as the source that can meet their deepest needs.

☐ ☐   3. God's Word, as revealed in Isaiah 55:1, teaches us that we can always petition God for help.

YOUR THOUGHTS ON DIFFERENTIATION

On the lines below, jot down your thoughts on the principle of differentiation. And write down some steps you can take to achieve a more differentiated marriage.

_____

_____

_____

_____

_____

_____

_____

_____

_____

_____

Day 4

SHARING GOD'S LOVE WITH THE RIGHT KIND OF CIRCUITRY

The one who trusts in the Lord will have faithful love surrounding him.

—

Psalm 32:10 Holman CSB

THOUGHT FOR THE DAY

Plug yourself directly into God . . . and encourage your mate to do the same. By connecting yourselves directly to the Father, you'll revolutionize your marriage.

D o you ever string up those little electric lights at Christmastime? If so, you've probably had this frustrating experience: One tiny light burns out, and the whole string of bulbs goes dark. Why does this happen? Because the lights are wired "in series," which means that for any of the bulbs to work, electricity must flow through all the bulbs. And if a single light bulb burns out, the whole string stops working.

Most married couples are wired like series circuits. If the husband feels blue or angry or disappointed, the wife does, too. And vice-versa. But there's a better strategy for marriage and for life: It's hooking one's self directly up to the Lord, not to one's mate.

Parallel circuits, unlike series circuits, continue to work even when one light stops burning. And that's exactly how you and your spouse should operate: You should both be connected with the Creator using parallel circuitry.

If you and your mate are each connected, first and foremost, to the Lord, then you both won't lose all your "juice" if your partner happens to blow a circuit.

So think of your marriage as a smartly-wired parallel circuit plugged directly into God's love. When you do, you'll never be disappointed . . . after all, His light never fails to shine.

A MARRIAGE TIP

Saturate yourself in the love of God, then you can pour out blessings on your mate.

SATURATED OR RUNNING ON EMPTY?

Are you saturated with God's love? If so, you'll have plenty for yourself and plenty to share with your mate.

There are several words for love in the ancient Greek language. There is "philio," which refers to brotherly love. There is "eros," which is used to describe sexual love. And there is "agape" love, which refers to God's love (or divine love). It is the agape love that powers the Christian's life. And it is agape love that will keep your marriage humming.

So love God with all your heart, soul, and mind. Let Him love you in return. Read His love letter to you. Each of you must fill your heart with His love for you. When you do, your marriage will be on the fast track to success.

The Christian way of life lends stability to marriage
because its principles and values naturally produce harmony.

—

James Dobson

LOVE THAT LASTS FOREVER

The Bible makes it clear that God's love for you and your spouse is deeper and more profound than either of you can imagine.

When you and your spouse embrace God together, both of you are forever changed. When you embrace God's love, you feel differently about yourself, your marriage, your family, and your world. When you join together and accept God's love, the two of you will be transformed.

So, if you and your mate genuinely want to build a love that endures, make God the focus of your marriage. When you do, your marriage will last forever—and so will your love.

Drinking In the Love of God

Read the following scriptures and write out your reflections on how God feels about you:

Isaiah 49:15-16

_____

_____

_____

_____

Psalm 40:5, Psalm 139:17-18

_____

_____

_____

_____

Lamentations 3:23-24

_____

_____

_____

_____

Matthew 13:45-46, inserting your name for the word "pearl" every time

_____

_____

_____

_____

QUESTIONS TO CONSIDER

1. In Jeremiah 2:13, God says that trying to satisfy yourself is like pouring water into a bowl which is _____.

2. In Isaiah 55:8, we are told that all people should turn to God because His thoughts are not our thoughts, and His _____ are not our _____.

True / False

☐ ☐ 3. When you are saturated in the love of God, you are then in a position to pour out your blessing on your spouse.

HOW MUCH TIME FOR GOD?

How much time are you and your mate spending each day with God? On the lines below, make notes about the quality—and quantity—of your spiritual life.

_____

_____

_____

_____

_____

_____

_____

_____

_____

_____

Day 5

LIGHTENING UP ON YOUR MATE, TIGHTENING UP WITH GOD

Trust in Him at all times, you people;
pour out your hearts before Him. God is our refuge. Selah

—

Psalm 62:8 Holman CSB

THOUGHT FOR THE DAY

Instead of griping to (or about) your mate, turn things over to God.
He can handle it!

Here's a perfect formula for improving your marriage: Lighten up on your mate and tighten up with God.

In the Book of Proverbs, we read that, "A word aptly spoken is like apples of gold in settings of silver" (25:11 NIV). This verse reminds us that the words we speak can and should be beautiful offerings to those we love. But sometimes, our communications, especially with our spouses, can be more discouraging than encouraging. And that's a problem, especially for couples who take their marriage vows seriously.

All of us have the power to enrich the lives of our loved ones. Sometimes, when we feel uplifted and secure, we find it easy to speak words of encouragement and hope. Other times, when we are discouraged or tired, we can scarcely summon the energy to uplift ourselves, much less anyone else. But, as loving Christians, our obligation is clear: We must always measure our words carefully as we use them to benefit others and to glorify our Father in heaven.

God intends that we speak words of kindness, wisdom, and truth, no matter our circumstances, no matter our emotions. When we do, we share a priceless gift with our loved ones, and we give glory to the One who gave His life for us. As believers, we must do no less.

So, the next time you are tempted to criticize your mate or demand that they change or be perfect in some way, catch yourself in the act and stop. Then turn your attention from your mate to your Heavenly Father. Put your hopes and expectations on Him. After all, He can handle things far better than you can.

Too Tough on Your Spouse? Are you being too hard on your mate? If so, it's time to lighten up before it's too late.

Husbands must learn to be strong without being demeaning or degrading. And wives must learn how to be supportive without being critical or controlling.

A MARRIAGE TIP

Quit trying to change your mate by nagging with your expectations. Refrain from being your spouse's constant critic; become your spouse's biggest booster.

Are You Patient Enough? Loving relationships inevitably require patience . . . plenty of patience. After all, we live in an imperfect world inhabited by imperfect people, so we need to be patient with everybody, especially our loved ones. Most of us, however, are perfectly willing to be patient with our spouses just as long as things unfold according to our own plans and according to our own timetables. In other words, we know precisely what we want, and we know precisely when we want it: right now, if not sooner.

As the old saying goes, "God gave everyone patience—wise people use it." But, for most of us, being patient with other folks is difficult. Why? Because we (like the "other folks") are fallible human beings, sometimes quick to anger and sometimes slow to forgive.

The next time you find your patience tested to the limit, slow down, calm down, and pray for guidance. And remember this: sometimes, we must wait patiently for our loved ones, and sometimes we must wait patiently for God. And that's as it should be. After all, think of how patient God has been with us.

When life is difficult, God wants us to have a faith
that trusts and waits.

—

Kay Arthur

 MARRIAGE EDITION

Questions to Consider

1. It's important to encourage your mate. You should be your spouse's biggest booster, not your spouse's constant _____.

2. If you want to improve your marriage, _____ up on your mate and _____ up with God.

True / False

☐ ☐   3. God wants you to be self-confident. He wants you to put all faith and confidence in yourself.

Think of ways that you've been hard on your spouse. Then, list several specific steps you can take to lighten up.

_____

_____

_____

_____

_____

When you're disappointed in your mate, how does God and His Word encourage you?

_____

_____

_____

_____

_____

_____

_____

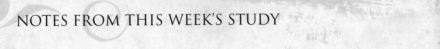

NOTES FROM THIS WEEK'S STUDY

Week 3

THE ROLE OF THE CHRISTIAN HUSBAND: TO LOVE, TO LEAD, TO LIVE

He who despises the word will be destroyed,
But he who fears the commandment will be rewarded.

—

Proverbs 13:13 NKJV

The Bible contains specific instructions for husbands. When married men obey God's Word, they are blessed, as are their wives. But when men disregard God's instructions, their marriages suffer. This week, we will examine what God's Word says about the responsibilities of the Christian husband. These responsibilities are: to love, to lead, to live.

God's Word makes it clear that the man is to be the leader of the family. Wise Christian men take that responsibility seriously . . . very seriously.

DAY 1: LOVE YOUR WIFE

DAY 2: LEAD YOUR WIFE

DAY 3: TREAT YOUR WIFE TENDERLY AND CAREFULLY

DAY 4: MEET YOUR WIFE'S NEEDS

DAY 5: HONOR YOUR WIFE

Day 1

LOVE YOUR WIFE

*Husbands, love your wives, just as also Christ loved the church
and gave Himself for her.*

—

Ephesians 5:25 Holman CSB

THOUGHT FOR THE DAY

God's Word clearly defines the role of the Christian husband: to love
their wives, to lead their wives, and to live with their wives.

God's Word leaves no room for doubt or interpretation: Husbands
are commanded to love their wives. So here's a question for all
you husbands: What does love mean to you? Is it simply a warm
feeling that you feel in the pit of your stomach when you see something
you like, or is it something more? Is it a fleeting burst of emotions that may
be here today and gone tomorrow, or is it something more? Is love merely a
strong physical attraction that you feel towards a woman whose appearance
you admire, or is it something more? If you answered "something more,"
you're right. Feelings of infatuation come and go, but genuine love isn't
like that—real love lasts.

Genuine love between a husband and a wife is meant to be patient,
understanding, consistent, and considerate. Genuine love doesn't just sit
around and do nothing; it is translated into acts of kindness. Genuine love
doesn't always spring up overnight, but it doesn't vanish overnight, either.
And, genuine love requires effort. Simply put, if you wish to build lasting
relationships, you must be willing to do your part.

Since the days of Adam and Eve, God has allowed His children to
make choices for themselves, and so it is with you. As you, a Christian
man, interact with your wife, you have many choices to make. If you
choose wisely, you'll be rewarded; if you choose unwisely, you'll bear the
consequences.

God does not intend for you to experience a mediocre marriage;
He created you and your bride for far greater things. Building lasting
relationships requires compassion, wisdom, empathy, kindness, courtesy,

and forgiveness (lots of forgiveness). If that sounds like work, it is—which is perfectly fine with God. Why? Because He knows that you are capable of doing that work, and because He knows that the fruits of your labors will enrich your marriage and the lives of generations yet unborn.

MESSAGE TO HUSBANDS

God joined you and your wife together. The Creator expects you to love your bride intimately, faithfully, without conditions, and without reservation.

---

10 RULES FOR CHRISTIAN HUSBANDS

1. The love you feel for your wife should be "agape" love: a divinely inspired love that reflects God's unconditional love for her.

2. Caring for your wife requires daily attention.

3. You can give without loving, but you can't love without giving.

4. You should encourage your wife's spiritual growth as she seeks to follow Christ, but you can't lead her there if you're unwilling to go yourself.

5. You must strive to love your wife as God loves you. That means that you must love her regardless of her response.

6. It's important that you provide for your wife and family, but giving material possessions is not enough; you must also give yourself to her.

7. You are to love your wife as you love yourself (Ephesians 5:28-33).

8. Take care of her needs, like you take care of your own. Ensure that your wife's needs for rest and exercise, spiritual growth, and clothing are met.

9. As a Christian husband, your purpose is to prepare her in order to present her to her eternal Groom, the Lord Jesus Christ (Revelations 19:7-8).

10. And last but not least, remember that love is a permanent commitment, not a transitory feeling.

LOVE GOD; LOVE YOUR WIFE

If you're a husband who genuinely wants to share greater intimacy with your wife, you'll first need to experience greater intimacy with God. The short Westminster Confession, in part, states, "the chief end of man is to worship God and enjoy Him forever." A dynamic, intimate relationship with God is the way to enjoy God. And the experience of intimacy with God is the source and springboard to joyful intimacy with your wife. Nehemiah 8:10 says, "The joy of the Lord is your strength." Through loving God, you are given a joyful strength to seek the highest good of your wife. This is what God intends for you to experience: vertical love with God which strengthens you to horizontally love your wife.

QUESTIONS TO CONSIDER

True / False

☐ ☐   1. God compares a man's love for his wife to Christ's love for the church.

☐ ☐   2. One of the best ways for a husband to help his wife grow spiritually is for the husband to grow spiritually himself.

3. Read Proverbs 31:10-31. List some of the ways that you, as a husband, can let your wife know that you love and appreciate her.

_____

_____

_____

_____

_____

_____

_____

_____

Husbands, is the love you feel for your wife conditioned upon her actions, or are you committed to her regardless of her response to you? Write down your thoughts on the lines below:

A little rain can strengthen
a flower stem.
A little love can change a life.

—

Max Lucado

Day 2

LEAD YOUR WIFE

*But I want you to know that Christ is the head of every man,
and the man is the head of the woman, and God is the head of Christ.*

—

1 Corinthians 11:3 Holman CSB

THOUGHT FOR THE DAY
God intends for men to lead their wives and their families, which means two things: men must take the initiative, and they must be involved.

OBSERVATIONS ABOUT THE LEADERSHIP ROLE OF THE CHRISTIAN HUSBAND

1. God intends for man to be the head of the household. This is God's divine design.
2. Leadership does not imply superiority over the wife or inequality. The leadership role simply describes the function of the man in his family.
3. A Christian leader is always a servant leader, so the role of a Christian husband is to serve His wife and children.
4. The mark of a leader is that he makes decisions. Sometimes this means that a man must be willing to step outside his comfort zone as he attempts to bring order out of chaos.
5. The wife needs protection and direction (1 Timothy 2:12-15), and the husband should provide it.
6. The wife will resist the husband's leadership (Genesis 3:16), but in spite of this fact, God still expects the husband to lead.
7. The Christian husband should never be detached from his family; he should always be engaged and involved, feeling the pulse of the family.

MESSAGE TO HUSBANDS

Your leadership role does not denote inequality between you and your wife. Your leadership role denotes responsibility to meet the needs of your wife and guide your family.

Why is it difficult for husbands to lead? For starters, husbands don't like rejection or resistance. It's natural for wives to resist their husband's leadership—that's just human nature. And because of sin, it's natural for wives to feel insecure about (and distrustful of) their husbands. Also, there are lots of confusing and chaotic situations in family life, and let's face it, men often don't know what is the right next step to take. That's why being a spiritual leader in the home is a challenge.

FINDING IT HARD TO BE A LEADER AT HOME?

Sometimes, as a husband, you may find it hard to assume the leadership role in your family, especially in a society that pushes secular values instead of God's values. After all, society stresses the equality of the sexes (while God celebrates the differences) and has put the leadership role of the man in doubt.

While you may find it helpful to read a few books on the principles of leadership, remember that the best book on Christian leadership is God's Book. Read it carefully, prayerfully, and often.

THOUGHTS ABOUT LEADERSHIP

You can never separate a leader's actions from his character.

—*John Maxwell*

The effective mentor strives to help a man or woman discover what they can be in Christ and then holds them accountable to become that person.

—*Howard Hendricks*

QUESTIONS TO CONSIDER

1. The mark of a leader is one who:

    A. Informs everyone that he is a leader;

    B. Reads books about leadership;

    C. Makes decisions;

    D. All of the above.

2. Who should be in charge of your marriage?

    The husband   The wife   God

True / False

☐ ☐   3. Real leadership means "being the boss" while making everyone in the family "toe the line."

Husbands, are you focused on the role of leading your wife and your family, come what may? Or do you sometimes take "the easy way out" by abdicating, at least temporarily, your responsibilities? Write down your thoughts on the lines below:

_____

_____

_____

_____

_____

_____

_____

_____

_____

Day 3

TREAT YOUR WIFE TENDERLY AND CAREFULLY

Husbands, in the same way, live with your wives with understanding of their weaker nature yet showing them honor as co-heirs of the grace of life, so that your prayers will not be hindered.

—

1 Peter 3:7 Holman CSB

THOUGHT FOR THE DAY
Christian husbands treat your wives tenderly, with understanding and discernment. That means husbands should be both gentle and wise.

Guys know from firsthand experience that we live in a rough-and-tumble society in which toughness is too often glamorized and tenderness is often scorned. Tenderness is often confused with weakness, which means that it's a trait many men avoid. But Christian men shouldn't be afraid to be tender.

It's important to remember that tenderness and toughness are not mutually exclusive. Jesus was gentle when He needed to be, but He certainly wasn't a shrinking violet, either. He was a carpenter by trade. He walked the dusty roads of Judea, preached to thousands, healed the sick, exorcized demons, and angrily confronted the money changers in the temple. Christ was a man's man who knew when to be strong and when to be gentle. The Son of God demonstrated time and again that "real" men can be gentle, kind, and loving. And that's exactly how God intends for real men to treat their wives. And if you sincerely want to be the kind of husband your wife deserves, you, too, should learn to be both tough and tender . . . when you need to be.

A WARNING TO MEN
Don't give your wife what you need . . . give her what she needs.

A MARRIAGE TIP

Kindness should be an integral part of your marriage every day, not just on the days when you feel good. And remember: small acts of kindness can make a big difference.

A FEW IMPORTANT NOTES FOR HUSBANDS

1. In 1 Peter 3:7, husbands are instructed to "live with their wives in an understanding way" (NASB) as they care for their "weaker vessel." Thus, women are, by nature, more vulnerable and more sensitive. And they should be treated more tenderly than men.
2. Because women are different from men (both emotionally and physically), God intends for women to be treated differently, especially by their husbands.
3. Husbands are instructed by God to meet the needs of their wives (1 Corinthians 7:33). Period.

QUESTIONS TO CONSIDER

1. In 1 Peter 3:7, we are taught that if a husband is to have an effective prayer life, he must _____ his wife.

2. Jesus was . . .

   A. Tough when He needed to be;

   B. Tender when He needed to be;

   C. Both of the above.

True / False

☐ ☐　3. It is an unwise husband who gives his wife what he needs, not what she needs.

Husbands, have you acquired the habit of always treating your wife tenderly, or are you sometimes a little less caring (or considerate) of your bride than you should be? Write down your thoughts on the lines below:

_____

_____

_____

_____

_____

_____

_____

When did I last run rough-shrod over her?

_____

_____

_____

_____

_____

_____

_____

> When you launch an act of kindness out into the crosswinds of life, it will blow kindness back to you.
>
> —
>
> *Dennis Swanberg*

NOTES

Day 4

MEET YOUR WIFE'S NEEDS

*A married man is concerned about the things of the world—
how he may please his wife.*

—

1 Corinthians 7:33 Holman CSB

THOUGHT FOR THE DAY

All wives have needs that God intends only husbands to meet. For Christian men, taking care of their wives isn't optional; it's mandatory.

Wives have many needs, but five of these needs require a husband's intentional attention:

1. **The Need for Affection:** It's "touch that means so much." Your wife needs tangible, physical touch from you, her man. When you come home, hug her. Rub her shoulders, hold her hand, snuggle up to her at night when you climb in bed. She will love it!

2. **The Need for Conversation:** Initiate talking with her. Ask her about her day before she asks you about yours. Ask her about the highs and the lows of her day. She will really appreciate you reaching out to connect with her through conversation.

3. **The Need for Openness and Honesty:** No closets, no secrets, no shadows. Be open with her about your life. She has committed herself to helping you in all of life, and she deserves to know you better than anyone else on the face of the earth. Never tell a half-truth . . . that amounts to a whole lie!

4. **The Need for Financial Support:** Husbands should not only earn money; they should also help their wives manage the money wisely. In 1 Timothy 3:8, Paul states clearly that a man who does not provide for his family has actually denied the Christian faith and has become worse than an unbeliever.

5. **The Need for Family Commitment:** This simply means that the best husband is a good father! Be involved and take the initiative with

your children. It will mean everything to your wife. Get involved with the kid's spiritual life, the physical discipline of the kids when you are home, and check on their schoolwork. It's fun to be involved with their extra-curricular activities as much as you possibly can. And you will make your wife so happy.

MEET YOUR SPOUSE'S NEEDS TODAY, NOT TOMORROW

It's easy to think about meeting your spouse's needs in the future. But the real question is this: How can you meet your spouse's needs to-day?

A WORD TO THE WISE

Some men enjoy the scripture verses that refer to the wife's submitting to her husband. These guys are quick to point out that the man should always wear the pants in the family, and that when he walks through the door of his "castle," the entire family ought to take care of his every need.

But the Bible also teaches us how a husband should love his wife: just as Christ loved the church. And that's a tall order—after all, the Son of God gave Himself for His bride (the church)—that means sacrifice!

So, Mr. Husband, the next time you begin to think that your wife needs to be more attentive to your needs, remember that you have biblically-defined responsibilities, too. As a Christian husband, you are to be like Christ, giving your life out of love for your wife. When you think about it that way, your responsibility to her is so profound that you'll naturally spend more time thinking about what you owe her, and less time worrying about what she owes you.

To the loved, a word of affection is a morsel,
but to the love-starved, a word of affection can be a feast.

—

Max Lucado

QUESTIONS TO CONSIDER

1. In 1 Corinthians 7:33 (Holman CSB) we are taught that a husband should seek to meet his wife's _____.

2. Husbands should strive to meet their wives' needs. Five things wives need are: _____, _____, _____, _____ support, and _____ commitment.

3. Husbands, how are you doing at meeting your wife's needs? Write each need and rate yourself on that need. (1-5, 1 being the worst, and 5 the best)

_____

_____

_____

_____

_____

_____

MEETING YOUR WIFE'S NEEDS

Now take a moment and think about your wife's needs, and on the lines below, list several steps you can take to better meet her needs.

_____

_____

_____

_____

_____

_____

Day 5

HONOR YOUR WIFE

Her sons rise up and call her blessed. Her husband also praises her:
"Many women are capable, but you surpass them all!"

—

Proverbs 31:28-29 Holman CSB

THOUGHT FOR THE DAY
Honor Your Spouse: Lift her up in the eyes of your family and others.

Have you ever heard a husband speak disparagingly of his wife? Perhaps he made his wife the butt of jokes, or maybe he complained about her shortcomings. Such comments are not productive, and they're never appropriate. Why? Because God's Word makes it clear that husbands must honor their wives, no exceptions.

Why are husbands sometimes so callous? All too often, men underestimate the importance of the words they speak (especially when their wives are absent). Yet whether guys realize it or not, their words carry great weight and great power, especially when they're talking about—or to—their loved ones.

The Bible reminds us that "Reckless words pierce like a sword, but the tongue of the wise brings healing" (Proverbs 12:18 NIV). And Christ taught that "Out of the abundance of the heart the mouth speaks" (Matthew 12:34 NKJV).

So here's a question for you, Mr. Husband: Does the abundance of your heart produce a continuing flow of praise for your wife? And, are you willing to hold your tongue when you feel the urge to begin an angry outburst? Hopefully so. After all, sometimes the most important words are the ones you don't speak.

If you want to build a better marriage—and if you want to keep building it day by day—honor your wife when she's with you or when you are with the guys. And give her just as much praise when you're at the kitchen table. Be like that important city leader in Proverbs who sang the praises of his wife for all to hear. When you do, you'll speak words that honor her and you—and you'll speak them often.

A WARNING TO HUSBANDS

You cannot pursue intimacy with God while demeaning your wife. So you must never, never, never demean your wife for any reason. Never.

MESSAGE TO HUSBANDS

Christian husbands are commanded (not advised, not encouraged . . . commanded!) to honor their wives. In fact, God's Word teaches that the way a husband treats his wife has a direct impact on his spiritual life.

Do you thank God each day for your wife? And, just as importantly, does your wife know that you're thanking God for her? If so, congratulations. If not, it's time for you to become a lot more thankful and a lot more vocal.

QUESTIONS TO CONSIDER

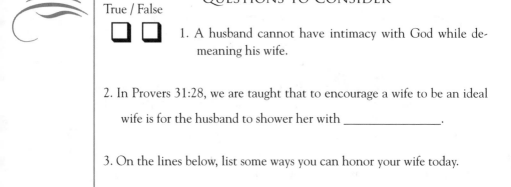

True / False

☐ ☐ 1. A husband cannot have intimacy with God while demeaning his wife.

2. In Proverbs 31:28, we are taught that to encourage a wife to be an ideal wife is for the husband to shower her with _____.

3. On the lines below, list some ways you can honor your wife today.

_____

_____

_____

_____

_____

_____

NOTES FOR HUSBANDS

In 1 Peter 3:7, we are taught that the way a husband treats his wife has a profound impact on his spiritual life. Husbands, on the lines below write down specific ways that your spiritual growth is affected by the way you treat your bride.

_____

_____

_____

_____

_____

_____

_____

_____

_____

_____

_____

_____

_____

_____

_____

_____

Your wife will prove
to be your greatest asset
if you value and honor her.

—

Stormie Omartian

NOTES FROM THIS WEEK'S STUDY

Week 4

THE ROLE OF THE CHRISTIAN WIFE

Charm is deceitful and beauty is passing,
But a woman who fears the Lord, she shall be praised.

—

Proverbs 31:30 NKJV

Just as God has given specific instructions to husbands, so, too, has He given divine guidance to wives. Wise women study God's Word and trust it. When married women obey God's Word, they are blessed, as are their husbands. But when women fail to respond to God's instructions, their marriages inevitably suffer. This week, we will consider what God's Word says about the responsibilities of the Christian wife. Wise wives will read and heed!

DAY 1: GOD'S DESIGN: A WIFE WHO HELPS AND COMPLETES

DAY 2: MEET YOUR HUSBAND'S SEXUAL NEEDS

DAY 3: BE HIS BEST FRIEND AND RECREATIONAL COMPANION

DAY 4: KEEPING THE HOME

DAY 5: ADMIRE YOUR HUSBAND

Day 1

GOD'S DESIGN: A WIFE WHO HELPS AND COMPLETES

"I will make a helper who is like him."

—

Genesis 2:18 Holman CSB

THOUGHT FOR THE DAY

God has clear instructions for Christian wives. They are to help, to nurture, to admire, and to complete their husbands.

The Bible clearly describes what it means to be a Christian wife. The Christian wife is designed by God to be a helper and a completer (Genesis 2:18). She supplies the missing pieces of her husband's puzzle; she complements her man; she completes his initiatives and enhances his creations. What the husband begins, the wife finishes and refines. Man provides the raw materials, and the woman polishes them.

As the helper and nurturer, the wife gives support from strength, not weakness. She must remember that woman was created by God because man needs woman to provide the customized help that only she can provide to help him become the man God wants him to be.

Woman was made for the man's sake (1 Corinthains 12:9). Why? Because he needs a helpmate, of course, but it doesn't stop there. He also needs the intimate, exclusive fellowship of his wife to nurture him. And because God gave man a strong ego, man needs admiration (Ephesians 5:33). And the best person to supply that admiration is his wife.

The Bible instructs wives to respond to husbands in submission (Ephesians 5:22-24, 1 Peter 3:5-6), but it's important to recognize that submission is not her role; it's her response to him, and it helps him fulfill his role as a servant leader. When a wife responds in this way, a husband is strengthened in his leadership and enjoys her companionship.

In summary, the Christian wife completes the husband. She is part of God's plan for his life; she makes him whole. No one can take her place. She is God's gift to her man today, tomorrow, and forever, amen.

A Message to Wives

Don't Confuse Helping with Inferiority: A helper gives support out of a sense of strength, not weakness. There is no indication of weakness or inferiority in the word "helper." The meaning refers to strength as in a military ally.

Questions to Consider

1. The submission the Bible speaks of is not the summation of the role of the woman, but the _____ of the woman to her man which helps him.

2. In Genesis 2:18 we are told that God created woman to be a companion to man and to be his _____.

True / False

☐ ☐ 3. The word "helpmate" implies weakness and inferiority.

Another Message to Women

Wives, nurture your husbands! And the Bible teaches you how to do it: Give them food, care, praise, and sex (Proverbs 31:11-12). Don't give your husband what you need; give him what he needs. Do good to him all the days of your life.

Wives, on the lines below, list three ways that you've been a good help-mate to your husband and three ways that you can become a better helper in the future.

_____

_____

_____

_____

_____

_____

_____

_____

_____

_____

_____

_____

_____

_____

Nothing bonds me closer to my husband than interceding
for him. If I sense my passion waning or my emotions sagging,
if I find myself pulling back from the demands of marriage,
I pray—for my husband.

—

Joni Eareckson Tada

Day 2

MEET YOUR HUSBAND'S SEXUAL NEEDS

A wife does not have authority over her own body, but her husband does. Equally, a husband does not have authority over his own body, but his wife does. Do not deprive one another—except when you agree, for a time, to devote yourselves to prayer. Then come together again; otherwise, Satan may tempt you because of your lack of self-control.

—

1 Corinthians 7:4-5 Holman CSB

THOUGHT FOR THE DAY

Spouses must strive to meet their partners' sexual needs or risk serious negative consequences, perhaps even tragic consequences. Your husband needs you to be his lover.

Okay, whether you're ready or not, it's time to talk about sex. More specifically, wives, it's time to talk about your husband's need for sex. He has physical needs, of course, and if you're wise, you'll meet those needs. But for him, sex is more than a physical act; your husband wants and needs to please you. He wants you to be his intimate (and involved) partner. When you nurture him by making sure that your sex life is healthy, he feels good about himself. But if you allow your sex life to deteriorate, he feels bad about himself, which is bad for him, and bad for you, too. You also open your husband up to temptation as he goes in the world.

Too many young wives today have no idea how important sex is to their husbands. After all, women are constructed differently than men, with different bodies and different psychological tendencies. So while wives may focus first on the emotional aspects of their marriage, men focus on the physical aspects first and the emotional aspects second. Sometimes, that means that as a wife, you may need to meet his needs even when you're exhausted or preoccupied, or both. When in doubt, just say yes.

Remember: part of nurturing your husband—a very important part—is making sure that his sexual needs are met. God intends for you, and you alone, to meet those needs. And your intentions should be the same.

A MESSAGE TO WIVES

Unmet sexual needs are one of the biggest causes of affairs, so work hard at meeting the needs that God intends for you alone to meet.

OBSTACLES TO SEX

1. **Body:** If you don't feel great about your body, you may not feel great about sex. But you should remember that your husband doesn't want your perfection; he wants your reckless abandon.
2. **Boredom:** Perhaps you're tired or just not in the mood. Even so, you'll be wise if you just say yes. Better yet, get your mind in gear. Plan ahead. Be creative and surprise him. You'll be amazed at how your desire will awaken.
3. **Baggage:** Perhaps you or your husband are burdened with emotional or physical baggage from previous sexual experiences that have left you wounded. If so, seek guidance from a godly counselor and look for help now. And remember that God's grace blots out every sin.

Okay wives, what if you're not totally satisfied with your body? (Who is?) Well here's a little secret: Your husband isn't looking for you to be a perfect 10; he delights in reckless abandon.

REMEMBER "THE TWO A'S

1. **Attack** him occasionally (by surprise, if you can). It means everything to a man to know that his wife desires to take the initiative from time to time.
2. **Be Available**: Just say yes. Even if you're exhausted, even if you're not totally in the mood, decide ahead of time that you won't turn him down. Once again, your willingness to be with him means everything to your man.

QUESTIONS TO CONSIDER

True / False

☐ ☐   1. One of the biggest causes of affairs is unmet needs.

☐ ☐   2. Wise Christian wives don't send their husbands out into this fallen world with their husbands' sexual needs unmet.

☐ ☐   3. Unless you're totally satisfied with your body, you won't have great sex.

Wives, if you've acquired the habit of regularly failing to meet your husband's sexual needs, can you explain why? And if you can't explain why, can you explain why you can't explain why? Got that? Jot down your thoughts on the lines below:

_____

_____

_____

_____

_____

_____

_____

_____

_____

_____

_____

_____

Day 3

BE HIS BEST FRIEND AND RECREATIONAL COMPANION

Then the Lord God said, "It is not good for the man to be alone."

—

Genesis 2:18a

THOUGHT FOR THE DAY

Your husband needs a best friend and a playmate, and that person should be you.

D o you want your marriage to be happy and healthy? Well here's a time-tested prescription for marital bliss: Make certain that your husband is your best friend and playmate.

Genuine friendship between a husband and wife should be treasured and nurtured. Remember God said it wasn't good for him to be alone—and so, He brought the woman to the man. Don't let all your husband's fun times be with the guys. Leave the housework and the kids and let him know you want to play with him. Many husbands feel they lose their wives as their best friend when the first baby arrives. So . . . be intentional and plan to put your husband first in the good times agenda. Memories of fun times shared together, just the two of you, is the glue that will help you stick together in the hard times of life.

Is your spouse your best friend? Do you guys laugh, love, and play together? And do you share some of the same hobbies? If so, you are immensely blessed by God—never take this gift for granted. So today, remember the important role that friendship plays in your marriage. And let your husband know you want to play together.

A MARRIAGE TIP

Invest in babysitters and plan ahead for those special occasions that infuse fun and spontaneity into the marriage.

ARE YOU TAKING CARE OF YOURSELF?

Remember: You are your husband's glory (1 Corinthians 11:7), so be sure to take care of yourself. Make sure that you resemble the person he married. And when you have questions concerning style, ask him what looks good to him.

> Remember, it takes time to build a friendship . . . even the friendship with your husband. So if you want your man to be your best friend, too, put him first, not the kids.

QUESTIONS TO CONSIDER

1. What are some ways you can become a fun companion to your husband?

    A. Make a list of possible fun activities;

    B. Set aside money for a babysitter;

    C. Plan a date doing something he loves to do.

    D. All of the above.

2. Do you ever have problems being a good "playmate" with your spouse? If so, why?

_____

_____

_____

_____

_____

_____

BECOMING A BETTER PLAYMATE

Every husband needs a playmate. List several ways you can become a better playmate.

_____

_____

_____

_____

_____

_____

_____

_____

_____

_____

Make a list of fun activities you might try together.

_____

_____

_____

_____

_____

_____

_____

_____

_____

_____

_____

Day 4

KEEPING THE HOME

She watches over the activities of her household and is never idle.

—

Proverbs 31:27 Holman CSB

THOUGHT FOR THE DAY

A good homemaker has a plan for managing her home; she honors her husband's homecoming; and she lives within her budget.

Wives are instructed by God to manage the home carefully and well (Proverbs 31). And that's as it should be. After all, our Heavenly Father is not a God of confusion or disorder; He has created an orderly universe, so we honor the Creator when we live orderly lives and keep orderly homes.

In the second chapter of Titus, God's Word instructs wives to be good homemakers. And savvy women are good managers who enlist the help of all able-bodied family members, including the man of the house. Your husband will appreciate knowing you are handling the home front well.

Homes don't magically organize themselves, and they don't stay organized without constant effort and attention. But wise women understand that when it comes to the art of making a home run smoothly, the payoffs are well worth the effort.

A MARRIAGE TIP

Use planning calendars, lists, and bulletin boards to keep everybody in your family informed of what's going on and who's doing what. Far more families suffer from "under-planning" rather than "over-planning."

THREE REASONS TO ORGANIZE YOUR HOME

1. A well-run home honors God (He is a God of order).

2. A well-run home helps your marriage (disorder creates chaos and chaos inevitably creates trouble).

3. A well-run home relieves emotional, physical, and financial stress.

A MESSAGE TO WIVES

Don't do it all yourself. Delegate! And in turn, family members should be ready and willing to follow the wife's direction without complaining (hey guys: are you paying attention, here?).

ON HONORING YOUR HUSBAND:
HIS HOMECOMING AND THE MONEY

You can be a great support to your husband by handling the home front well. Just being prepared to greet him when he returns home will make him feel like a king even for just a few minutes. Wives have the power to set the atmosphere and the attitude of the family toward Dad. "Daddy's home!" (with a joyful smile) or "Your father is finally home . . . ugh!" Greet him with a smile and a hug. Get off the phone. And don't be surprised if your little ones join the group hug.

You can also honor him while he's striving to be the best provider by living within your budget (no matter how large or small it is). Don't sabotage his efforts to provide by charging up big debt.

Woman are encouraged in scripture to learn practical home management skills from wise Christian women. Who are you learning from?

QUESTIONS TO CONSIDER

1. Titus 2:5 teaches us that whatever else a wife does, she should be a good

   _____.

2. A well-run home . . .

   A. Honors God.

   B. Improves the marriage.

   C. Relieves stress.

   D. All of the above.

3. As a homemaker what is most difficult for you: planning, organizing, delegating, or implementing? Why?

   _____

   _____

   _____

   _____

   _____

   _____

   _____

The secret of a happy home life is that the members
of the family learn to give and receive love.

—

Billy Graham

Men have differing expectations about what it means to have an organized home. How does your husband interpret your support as a homemaker? And what things can you do around the house that mean the most to him?

_____

_____

_____

_____

_____

_____

_____

_____

_____

_____

_____

_____

_____

_____

_____

_____

_____

_____

_____

_____

_____

_____

_____

_____

Day 5

ADMIRE YOUR HUSBAND

To sum up, each one of you is to love his wife as himself,
and the wife is to respect her husband.

—

Ephesians 5:33 Holman CSB

THOUGHT FOR THE DAY

Your husband needs (and deserves) a world-class cheerleader. As his wife, you need (and deserve) to fill that role.

Face facts: God gave your husband an ego, perhaps a man-sized ego, so he could go out and conquer and achieve. So your husband wants to feel good about himself and his accomplishments. But out there in the real world, where he goes five or six days a week to earn a living for your family, his ego is sometimes beaten down. After all, it's tough to get ahead today, and even tougher to stay ahead. So when your man returns home after a hard day's work (and perhaps after a few ego-deflating experiences), he needs respect, admiration, and praise. And it's your job, as his wife, to make sure he gets it. God's command is clear to wives: respect your husband.

Every husband needs for his wife to be his #1 cheerleader. No other person on earth can build up a man like his wife, and no other person on earth can tear him down like his wife. So don't take your husband for granted. Verbalize your appreciation and admiration. And while you're at it, make sure that you don't make your admiration conditional. You do not respect him because he has earned it, but because God commands it. Anyway, it's God's job to refine him, not yours! In other words, don't withhold your praise just because you want your man to "shape up." Instead of being a part-time cheerleader, go all out.

What's a good way to make sure that you're giving your husband the respect he deserves? A great place to start is by focusing on his (many) strengths, not his (few) negative qualities. After all, your husband doesn't just want your admiration, he needs it. And for that matter, you deserve the joyful experience of giving it to him. No one can light up his face like you, paying attention to him and noticing the good things he does.

Remember: You are the one woman in all the world God picked out to meet his needs. Nobody can do it better.

A MESSAGE TO WIVES

Wives, if you're serious about nurturing your husband, build him up. No one can build him up like you, and no one can bring him down like you. Admiration and appreciation will motivate him. Criticism will rob him of motivation. It doesn't matter to him if everyone else is cheering him on, if you're not. He would rather have your admiration than a payraise.

QUESTIONS TO CONSIDER

1. When Paul sums up the responsibilities of a wife in Ephesians 5:33, he instructs her to _____ her husband.

True / False

☐ ☐   2. A wife is best positioned to build her husband up, and, if she chooses, to tear him down.

☐ ☐   3. It's enough to just think your husband is wonderful. Feeling this might make him proud.

ANOTHER MESSAGE TO WIVES

Don't try to "fix" your husband. Your job is to respect him, and God's job is to refine him.

Wives, every man needs a cheerleader, and you must fill that role for your husband. On the lines below, make a list of his strengths. Keep writing until you fill up the page (and it's perfectly acceptable to add extra sheets of paper, if needed!). Then, plan to start sharing those strengths, starting tonight when you climb in bed.

_____

_____

_____

_____

_____

_____

_____

_____

_____

_____

_____

_____

_____

_____

_____

_____

_____

_____

_____

_____

_____

_____

_____

_____

Week 5

BUILDING COMMUNICATION SKILLS

The words of the wise bring healing.

—

Proverbs 12:18 NLT

How many marriages have been undermined by the fact that neither husband nor wife possessed solid communication skills? Plenty of marriages.

This week, we'll consider communication strategies that work. And we'll pay particular attention to the role that conflict management plays in every successful marriage.

///////////////////////////////////

DAY 1: COMMUNICATION SKILLS FOR MEN

DAY 2: COMMUNICATION SKILLS FOR WOMEN

DAY 3: HANDLING CONFLICT

DAY 4: EIGHT PRACTICAL PRINCIPLES OF CONFLICT MANAGEMENT

DAY 5: CONFLICT SHARING AND CREATIVE SOLUTIONS

Day 1

COMMUNICATION SKILLS FOR MEN

My dearly loved brothers, understand this: everyone must be quick to hear, slow to speak, and slow to anger.

—

James 1:19 Holman CSB

THOUGHT FOR THE DAY

Learning to communicate effectively is essential to a healthy marriage. Without clear communication, husbands and wives feel isolated and misunderstood.

It probably comes as no surprise by now that men and women see things differently. So it's not too shocking that they communicate differently, too. Problems arise when men employ a "guy-to-guy" communication style. To avoid this predicament, here are four things that husbands can do to become better communicators at home:

1. Learn to Listen

Men decide what they think before they talk; women decide what they think while they're talking. So it's important for women to know they're being heard, especially when they're speaking to their husbands. So a wise husband:

    A. Seeks out his wife when he comes home;
    B. Asks her about her day;
    C. Doesn't take it personally if she's upset;
    D. Asks additional questions and lets her know he's engaged by giving some verbal cues.

2. Refuse to Be "Mr. Fix It"

When women share their feelings, most husbands view it as a call to action (which means that caring husbands may drop everything in order to seek an immediate solution). But many times, when women share their feelings, they simply want to be understood; in such cases, problem-solving is of secondary importance. So savvy husbands learn to listen first and problem-solve later (if necessary).

3. Give Reassurance

A woman interprets silence or withdrawal as rejection, so don't be silent and don't withdraw. And if you have to leave for an appointment, give words of reassurance, i.e. "Honey, I'll be back and we will pick up where we left off."

4. Ask for Her Input

Ask and ye shall receive; don't ask and you may not.

A MARRIAGE TIP

Communication is vital to the health of any relationship. If you're having trouble expressing yourself, don't clam up. Instead, keep trying until you finally get the hang of it. Maybe try writing your feelings first.

Husbands, Listen Early, Often, and Carefully: Are you in the habit of listening to your bride? Do you listen carefully (not superficially), and do you take time to think about the things that you hear and identify? If so, you're building a stronger marriage. But if you allow the obligations of everyday living to interfere with the communication you share with your wife, it's time to reorder your priorities. Now!

Don't Fan the Flames: When your spouse becomes angry or upset, you'll tend to become angry and upset, too. Resist that temptation. Keep your cool, and let her vent. By not fanning the flame, you'll help her lose her upsetness.

 MARRIAGE EDITION

Questions to Consider

1. Husbands can better communicate with their wives by:

   A. Seeking her out when he comes home.

   B. Asking her about her day.

   C. If she becomes upset, not taking it personally.

   D. All of the above.

True / False

☐ ☐   2. A woman usually reaches out to connect by using logic and reason.

☐ ☐   3. Men usually decide things first and then, only after they've decided, do they begin talking. Women, on the other hand, often make decisions while they're talking.

Husbands: On the lines below, list some specific ways you can become a better communicator with your wife.

_____

_____

_____

_____

_____

_____

_____

_____

_____

A Reminder to Husbands: Wives "connect" by sharing their feelings. So don't give solutions; give understanding. Try to identify and reassure.

Day 2

COMMUNICATION SKILLS FOR WOMEN

From a wise mind comes wise speech; the words of the wise are persuasive.

—

Proverbs 16:23 NLT

THOUGHT FOR THE DAY

Wise wives learn how to improve the way they say things so they will really connect with their husbands.

Wives, if you'd like better communication with your husband, it helps to understand how he thinks and what makes him tick. The following simple strategies will help you communicate more effectively with your man:

1. Give Him Appreciation

A man is motivated by appreciation and accomplishment. He wants to be his wife's problem solver hero! But if the woman's elaboration increases, the man's frustration multiplies. So wives, be sure that you don't talk problems to death. Instead, assure your hubby that you know he can handle it. And if you simply must keep talking, thank him for helping you by listening, and be sure he's knows you're not blaming him.

2. Refuse to Give Unsolicited Advice

In a man's world, it's honorable for your husband to handle things by himself. Your man wants to be your knight in shining armor, and it's your job to let him. Here's how:

A. Accept Him, Don't Correct Him (Proverbs 19:13)
B. Encourage Him, Don't Criticize Him (Proverbs 12:4)
C. Stop Trying to Change Him (2 Samuel 6)

Instead of being judgmental or critical, appeal to his character and his competency. And when it comes to changing him, leave that up to God.

3. Learn to Ask for Help

Don't expect your husband to be a mind reader (remember that he doesn't have your woman's intuition). Men don't normally offer help unless they're asked, so ask. When you make your request, be brief, be direct, and learn to ask by using the words, "will you" or "would you," not "can you" or "could you."

When you take the above advice, you'll communicate more effectively and more easily with your hubby . . . and everybody wins.

Wives Remember This: Cutting your husband down with words will stunt his growth into the godly man you want him to be.

A MARRIAGE TIP

Admiration is contagious. Words of praise will lift him up and they just might come back to lift you up.

Words. Do you fully understand their power?
Can any of us really grasp the mighty force behind
the things we say? Do we stop and think before we speak,
considering the potency of the words we utter?

—

Joni Eareckson Tada

Don't Be a Chronic Complainer: You'll never whine your way to a happy marriage, so don't even try.

QUESTIONS TO CONSIDER

1. In a man's world, it's honorable to handle things by _____.

2. In communicating a request to her husband, a wife should:

    A. Be brief;

    B. Be direct;

    C. Use words like "will you" or "would you," not "can you" or "could you."

    D. All of the above.

True / False

☐ ☐   3. When a wife makes a request of her husband, the more words she uses, the better.

Wives: On the lines below, list some specific ways you can become a better communicator with your husband.

_____

_____

_____

_____

_____

_____

_____

_____

_____

_____

_____

Day 3

HANDLING CONFLICT

Patience is better than power, and controlling one's temper,
than capturing a city.

—

Proverbs 16:32 Holman CSB

THOUGHT FOR THE DAY

All couples experience conflict. Wise couples learn to address conflict and resolve it; other couples avoid conflict and suffer the consequences.

B ecause we are all fallen people living in a fallen world, we have conflict both inside and outside our marriages. Because women and men have different motivations and needs, it's inevitable that every couple encounters conflict. Wise couples learn to resolve conflict before their disagreements drive them apart.

THREE OBSERVATIONS ABOUT CONFLICT

1. Conflict Is Inevitable: Because we're human, we have disagreements—if we're wise, we don't suppress anger; we address it and resolve it.

2. Conflict Is a Pivotal Obstacle: It is a wedge that either drives a couple apart or brings them closer together. Unresolved conflicts build a wall between partners, leaving them alone and isolated in marriage.

3. Conflict Is Manageable: Savvy couples address conflict ASAP. Not-so-savvy couples sweep things under the rug and sow the seeds of destruction in their marriages.

If two people agree on everything,
one of them is unnecessary.

—

Ruth Bell Graham

A Few More Observations About Conflict

1. When conflicts arise, it's tempting to withdraw, either physically (by vacating the premises) or emotionally (by tuning out). But withdrawal is a terrible way to resolve conflict, especially in marriage.
2. When conflicts arise between husbands and wives, it's tempting for the woman to give in because she thinks (wrongly) that giving in is the best way to make her marriage work. But when a woman suppresses her feelings, she becomes embittered and withdrawn—and she harms the marriage far more than she helps it.
3. Compromise isn't all it's cracked up to be. After all, compromise doesn't work if one person is 100% correct and the other is 100% wrong.
4. Trying to win an argument causes communication to stop. Learn to listen and let your spouse complete their thought without cutting them off or down.

Unresolved Conflict Is Dangerous

Unresolved conflict: 1. Destroys relationships 2. Causes affairs and divorces 3. Creates life-threatening internal stresses.

Questions to Consider

True / False

☐ ☐   1. The best marriages have no conflict.

2. Conflict either makes couples _____ or drives them _____.

3. What are some of the problems with unresolved conflict that you have experienced?

_____

_____

_____

_____

_____

A MARRIAGE TIP

The refusal to love, including the refusal to reconcile relationships, is sin.

Think about the way your parents dealt with conflict. Did they address it or ignore it? Did one parent always win and the other always yield? Did one or both parents withdraw? Or did they actually manage conflict well? And how did their conflict-management style effect the way you manage conflict? Write your thoughts on the lines below:

_____

_____

_____

_____

_____

_____

_____

_____

_____

_____

_____

_____

_____

Conflict can become either
the source of greater intimacy or
the source of greater isolation.

—

Ed Young

Day 4

Eight Practical Principles of Conflict Management

Don't be quick-tempered, for anger is the friend of fools.

—

Ecclesiastes 7:9 NLT

Thought for the Day

When you encounter conflict in your marriage, you can resolve it, and that's exactly what you and your mate should strive to do. Today, we'll consider eight practical steps that are sure to help.

Eight Practical Principles for Resolving Conflict

The following techniques must be applied in the midst of a conflict. So if you find yourself in the midst of conflict, call timeout, step back, and agree to play by the following rules:

1. **Don't Use Explosive Terms:** Words like "never" and "always" may seem appropriate in the heat of a conflict, but they're not.

2. **Absolutely No Name-calling (Ephesians 4:29):** It's surprising how many believers revert to their pre-Christian days when it comes to the language they use in the midst of a conflict. So when in doubt, hold your tongue before you say something that can't be unspoken.

3. **Do Not Interrupt (Proverbs 18:13):** Of course, you'll be sorely tempted to butt in, especially if the conflict is intense. Or you'll be tempted to ignore what your spouse is saying because you're trying to think about what you'll say next. But don't interrupt . . . and do listen.

4. **Attack the Problem, Not the Person (Romans 18:10):** Stay on topic, be devoted, and don't rehash past offenses. Remember that problems come and go, but the people stay.

5. Own Your Own Feelings: Use "I", not "you" (Gen. 3:10, 12). Overusing the "you" word puts your mate on the defensive (and that's not where you want your mate to be).

6. Settle It by Bedtime (Ephesians 4:26): Don't go to bed angry, and if you can't settle everything, calm down and agree to work cooperatively on the problem in the morning. If you make and keep this simple pledge, you'll protect your intimacy and you won't allow Satan to gain a foothold by dividing you and your spouse. By the way, this simple rule is one of the most important commitments you'll make in your marriage.

7. Remember: The issue is probably not the real issue (the real issue is how you two are communicating).

8. When You're Wrong, Ask for Forgiveness: Don't just say "I'm sorry"— ask to be forgiven. And remember this: There's a difference between saying you're sorry and asking for forgiveness. A BIG difference.

A MARRIAGE TIP

External anger slept on becomes internal bitterness in the morning.

QUESTIONS TO CONSIDER

1. Ephesians 4:29 (NKJV) teaches us that we should use our words for the purpose of _____ others up.

2. In resolving conflict, one should always attack the problem, not the

_____.

True / False

☐ ☐   3. When it comes to managing conflict, one of the most important things you and your mate can do is agree to settle things before you go to bed at night.

> *Don't let the sun go down on your anger,*
> *and don't give the Devil an opportunity.*
>
> —
>
> *Ephesians 4:26-27 Holman CSB*

Think about the last big conflict you had with your spouse. How did you handle it, and how might you have handled it better? Write down your thoughts on the lines below:

_____

_____

_____

_____

_____

_____

_____

_____

_____

_____

_____

_____

_____

_____

_____   Whatever you do when conflicts
                                  arise, be wise. Fight against
_____   jumping to quick conclusions and
                                  seeing only your side. There are
_____   always two sides on the streets of
                                  conflict. Look both ways.
_____
                                            —
_____
                                      Charles Swindoll

Day 5

CONFLICT SHARING AND CREATIVE SOLUTIONS

My dear brothers and sisters, be quick to listen,
slow to speak, and slow to get angry.
Your anger can never make things right in God's sight.

—

James 1:19-20 NLT

THOUGHT FOR THE DAY

Communicating in the midst of a conflict can often be painful . . . but remember, there is no intimacy apart from pain.

When you're involved in a conflict, it's tempting to convince yourself that the problem belongs 100% to the other person. A better strategy, however, is to share the problem and look for creative solutions together. Conflict resolution gets easier over time, but it will never be easy.

In the heat of an argument, it's tempting to blame your mate for anything and everything. Tempting but wrong. A better strategy is to share the conflict and to look for creative solutions. Here's how:

Identify an Issue

1. Identify one recent issue that has caused conflict between you and your mate.

Understand Your Mate's Position

2. Husbands: Invite your wife to share her feelings and thoughts first. Listen to her and don't interrupt.
3. Wives: Ask your husband to share his thoughts and feelings on the same issue.
4. Husbands: Verbalize what you think your wife has said. Ask her if you're correct. If not, ask her to clarify her feelings.

5. Wives: Restate his feelings and ask for clarification.
6. How does it feel to really understand each other? Talk about your emotional response to one another in the midst of the discussion (remember: the issue is not the issue; the issue is how you're communicating).

Be Creative Together

7. Having discussed your feelings, decide if there's a need for a solution. Then, offer several possible alternatives.

Choose the Best Solution

8. Choose together the best solution (a solution that both of you are comfortable with). You have arrived at resolution. You have resolved your conflict.
9. If you are unable to choose a solution you are both comfortable with, agree to wait for a time of further communication.

A MARRIAGE TIP

Forgive and Keep Forgiving: If you're having trouble forgiving your mate for some past mistake or shortcoming, think of all the times your loved ones have forgiven you! (1 Peter 4:8).

When considering your spouse's imperfections, don't lose sight of your own: If your mate isn't perfect—and he isn't—remember that your sweetheart can say the same thing about you. So don't expect perfection from anybody, and that includes the people who live under your roof.

Those who abandon ship the first time it enters a storm miss
the calm beyond. And the rougher the storms weathered together,
the deeper and stronger real love grows.

—

Ruth Bell Graham

QUESTIONS TO CONSIDER

1. Sometimes, if you can't reach a comfortable mutually agreeable solution, the best thing to do is simply to _____ for a while and give everybody a chance to cool off and catch their breath.

2. In James 1:19-20 (NLT) we are told that we should be _____ to listen and _____ to speak.

True / False

☐ ☐ 3. Husbands who listen carefully to their wives are likely to understand immediately (and without clarification) what their wives are trying to communicate.

YOUR NOTES ON CONFLICT SHARING AND CREATIVE SOLUTIONS

_____

_____

_____

_____

_____

_____

_____

_____

_____

_____

_____

_____

_____

NOTES FROM THIS WEEK'S STUDY

Week 6

'TIL DEBT DO US PART: MANAGING MONEY

The one who acquires good sense loves himself;
one who safeguards understanding finds success.

—

Proverbs 19:8 Holman CSB

Countless books have been written about money—how to make it and how to keep it. But if you're a Christian, you probably already own at least one copy—and probably several copies—of the world's foremost guide to financial security. That book is the Holy Bible. God's Word is not only a roadmap to eternal life; it is also an indispensable guidebook for life here on earth. As such, the Bible has much to say about your life, your faith, and your finances.

If your family is in need of a financial makeover, God's Word can help. In fact, Biblical principles can help you organize your financial life and, at the same time, improve your marriage. When you learn to control money (before it controls you), you and your mate will have less need to worry and more time to celebrate God's glorious creation. In the Bible, more is written about money and stewardship than about heaven and hell combined. So dig in to the riches of God's Word this week as you study this week's lesson.

DAY 1: THE IMPORTANCE OF MANAGING MONEY IN A MARRIAGE

DAY 2: VALUES-BASED MONEY MANAGEMENT

DAY 3: HAVE A BUDGET AND STICK TO IT

DAY 4: LIVE ON CASH, NOT DEBT

DAY 5: SUMMING IT UP: GOD'S PLAN FOR YOUR MARRIAGE

Day 1

THE IMPORTANCE OF MANAGING MONEY IN A MARRIAGE

Wherever your treasure is, there your heart and thoughts will also be.

—

Matthew 6:21 NLT

THOUGHT FOR THE DAY

Money problems, when allowed to multiply, can create disharmony and dissatisfaction within a marriage. So wise husbands and wives take a proactive approach to money management.

Experts agree that money problems are a major cause of marital problems and perhaps the number-one cause of divorce. So savvy couples are serious about money management. If you want to minimize the hassles and heartaches that accompany financial distress, you and your mate will learn to handle your money maturely.

Thankfully, the basic principles of money management aren't too tough to understand: Live on a budget; make more than you spend; give God His fair share; own your own home (when you can afford it, not before), and avoid consumer debt like a ready-to-strike rattlesnake. Work together to make sure that you and your spouse are on the same page about the finances—and that it's the right page.

God's Word is filled with principles for successful living, including effective money management. So if you'd like to improve your finances, or any other aspect of your life, apply God's instruction book and use a heaping helping of good old-fashioned common sense. It's the very best way to live.

Nearly 80% of divorced couples between 20 and 30 stated that financial problems were the primary cause of their divorce.

—

Larry Burkett

A Thought About True Security

You can't fully enjoy financial peace . . . until you fully accept God's peace personally; then God's plan financially.

Diligent to Work and Diligent to Save

In Proverbs 6:7-8 the wisest man on earth commends the ant for his initiative in working and saving for the future without anyone telling him what to do. Are you willing to save money and invest for the future, or do you feel compelled to spend every penny you make? The answer to this question will determine, to a surprising extent, the state of your financial health today and the state of your financial health in the future.

If you're spending everything you make today while saving nothing for tomorrow, don't be surprised if, when tomorrow comes, your bank balance approximates zero. But, if you form the habit of saving some money each month, you'll soon discover that the old adage is true: the more you save, the more you'll have.

Are you already saving money from your paycheck each month? And are you investing that money in sound, get-rich-slow kinds of investments? (Ecclesiastes 5:10-14) If so, you are wise. If not, remember this: it's never too late to start saving for the future. And the more quickly you do so, the sooner you'll achieve your financial goals.

A Marriage Tip

Save for the future.

Your priorities, passions, goals, and fears
are shown clearly in the flow of your money.

—

Dave Ramsey

QUESTIONS TO CONSIDER

1. You can't fully enjoy financial peace until you accept _____

   peace.

True / False

☐ ☐   2. The Bible doesn't have very much to say about the topic
   of money.

☐ ☐   3. Saving for the future is a good idea only if you have extra
   money.

Are you satisfied with the way you and your spouse manage money? If so,
congratulations. If not, write down some ideas about ways that you both
might improve your money management skills.

_____

_____

_____

_____

_____

_____

_____

_____

_____

_____

_____

_____

_____

_____

_____

Day 2

VALUES-BASED MONEY MANAGEMENT

Honor the Lord with your possessions, and with the firstfruits of all your increase; so your barns will be filled with plenty.

—

Proverbs 3:9-10 NKJV

THOUGHT FOR THE DAY

Most of us would say that among our top financial responsibilities are giving and saving for the future. But our checkbooks and credit card statements reveal our true values, which may be very different from our stated priorities.

I f you asked most of us to name our top financial responsibilities, we'd probably put giving near the top. But our checkbooks often tell a different story. Most Americans, including Christians, make supporting their lifestyle the top priority. Their second priority is debt repayment (which is a result of their lifestyle). Third place goes to Uncle Sam in the form of taxes (not optional). Accumulation of wealth winds up in fourth place, and giving, sadly enough, brings up the rear.

The content of your character is demonstrated by the way you choose to spend your money. If you honor God first with your money and then use the rest wisely, then you're doing fine. But if you're up to your eyeballs in debt, and if "shop till you drop" is your unofficial motto, it's time to retire those credit cards and rearrange your priorities.

Our society is in love with money and the things that money can buy. We think this is where life really is, but it's not. A man's true life isn't made up of the things he owns, no matter how rich he may be (Luke 12:15). God values people, not possessions, and so should we.

Money, in and of itself, is not evil; worshipping money is. So today, as you and your spouse prioritize matters of importance, remember that God is almighty, but the dollar is not (1 Timothy 6:10). Then, manage your budget—and your donations—accordingly.

A MARRIAGE TIP

Your value system will determine how you earn, how you spend, and how you save money: So make certain that your value system is built upon the firm foundation of God's wisdom and God's Word.

Christian stewardship may be defined as "the proper management of one's resources for the glory of God." And, for thoughtful believers, stewardship is the foundation of any financial plan.

As Christians, we are challenged to be faithful stewards of the resources and talents that God has given us. But we live in a world that encourages us to do otherwise.

Ours is a society that is filled to the brim with countless opportunities to squander our time, our talents, and our money. All of us have special gifts, and you are no exception. Today, accept this challenge: value the talent that God has given you, nourish it, make it grow, and share it with the world. For dedicated believers like you, stewardship is not something to be taken lightly. After all, God has given you a wide array of opportunities and a special set of abilities. That's why you must manage your resources as if they were a one-of-a-kind treasure on loan from God, which, by the way, they are (Matthew 25:29).

MORE GREAT THOUGHTS ABOUT MONEY

The Christian way of life lends stability to marriage
because its principles and values naturally produce harmony.

—

James Dobson

Values affect the inflow and the outflow of money.

—

Dave Ramsey

QUESTIONS TO CONSIDER

1. In Proverbs 3:9, we are told that we should use our wealth to honor the

_____.

2. What affects how you earn, spend, and save money?

    The Latest Trend   Your Values   The Government

Why do you think money is such a volatile issue in many marriages? Jot your thoughts down here.

_____

_____

_____

_____

_____

_____

_____

_____

Are you honoring God first with your money? Why or why not?

_____

_____

_____

_____

_____

_____

Day 3

HAVE A BUDGET AND STICK TO IT

The plans of the diligent certainly lead to profit,
but anyone who is reckless only becomes poor.

—

Proverbs 21:5 Holman CSB

THOUGHT FOR THE DAY

The foundation of your family's financial plan is a written budget that you and your spouse agree upon.

Far too many people "never quite get around" to making a budget. Why? Oftentimes, it's because these folks are afraid of the things that their budgets might reveal. Members of the non-budget crowd tell themselves that they're simply "too busy to budget" or that they're "bad with numbers." But in truth, these people are worried that their budgets might contain bad news; they're fearful that the cold hard facts may be too cold and too hard to take. But when it comes to money matters, ignorance is never bliss.

If you've been putting off the job of formulating your household budget, ask yourself why. And then, after that long embarrassing pause while you struggle, unsuccessfully, for a logical answer, start the budgeting process . . . now!

Creating a budget is relatively easy. No matter how large or small your income, you need to be intentional about how you spend it. You need a plan. So make a plan determining ahead of time where your money is going to be spent (Proverbs 21:5). Living by that budget can be considerably harder because life on a budget demands discipline and self-sacrifice. If you find yourself struggling to live within your means, perhaps you need a significantly larger dose of wisdom from the ultimate guidebook on disciplined living: the Holy Bible.

So instead of spending now and worrying about it later, make a budget that makes sense. And live by it. When you do, you'll spend less time worrying and more time celebrating your life and your marriage. And that, by the way, is precisely what God wants you to do.

What follows is a model budget that you may find helpful:

MODEL OF HOUSEHOLD BUDGET

Fixed Expenditures (_____/mo.)

Lord _____

House _____

Utilities _____

   Gas _____

   Water _____

   Electricity _____

   Phone _____

   Cable _____

   Newspaper _____

Insurance _____

   Car _____

   Life _____

   Lessons _____

   Car Payment _____

Long-Term Savings (_____)

IRA _____/mo.

Investments _____

Christmas _____

Vacation _____

College _____

Wedding _____

Family Entertainment (_____/mo.)

Short-Term Savings (_____)

Car Repairs _____

Car Registrations _____

House Repairs _____

Furniture Purchases _____

Yard Maintenance _____

(Keep in Cash) _____

Individual Budgets (_____/mo.)

Husband _____

Wife _____

Child _____

Child _____

Child _____

Household Budgets (_____/mo.)

Groceries _____

Seasonal Decorations _____

Household Supplies _____

Personal Budgets (One for each member of the family, age 10 and up)

Lord _____

Savings _____

Clothing _____

Gifts _____

Spending _____

A MARRIAGE TIP

Unless you have clairvoyant powers (and you don't), it is wise to leave room in your budget for unexpected little surprises.

On the lines below, make notes about how you plan to use a budget in your household. Will the two of you . . . plan to have meetings (not arguments) about how to spend or save your earnings? Discuss any purchase over a certain amount? Pray together about how best to use your money?

_____

_____

_____

_____

_____

_____

_____

_____

_____

_____

_____

_____

_____

_____

_____

_____ Budgeting is telling your money
                                where to go instead of
_____ asking it where it went.

_____ —

                                John Maxwell

114

Day 4

LIVE ON CASH, NOT DEBT

The borrower is a slave to the lender.

—

Proverbs 22:7 Holman CSB

THOUGHT FOR THE DAY

Since the borrower is servant to the lender, it's best to live on a cash basis, not on credit.

Whether you're buying a mattress, a microwave, or a Maserati, somebody will probably be willing to sell it to you on credit. But the Bible makes it clear that the instant you become a debtor, you also become a slave to the lender (Proverbs 22:7). So do yourself and your family a favor by putting you and your family on a cash budget. What does that mean? It means that you never buy consumer goods such as clothes, furniture, or electronics on credit. It means you don't buy things with credit cards. And it means that even if the interest rate seems incredibly attractive, you don't sign your name on the dotted line; you wait until you can afford to pay cash for the things you buy. And what if you run out of cash before payday? You stop spending.

To sum it up, incurring debt has few benefits and many bad effects. So beware. And if you're trying to decide whether or not to make that next big purchase, remember that when it comes to borrowed money, less is more . . . much more.

Establish a Cash Cushion: How much cash do you need in your "rainy day" fund? That depends upon your current income, your current level of expenses, and the time that it might take you to find new work if you were to find yourself "between" jobs. Sit down with your spouse and determine how much cash you need in your account to sleep comfortably at night. And then don't buy another big ticket item until you've saved that amount.

A Marriage Tip

Avoid a financial collapse—stay out of debt.

---

9 Steps for Getting Yourself Out of Debt

1. Pray

2. Establish a written budget

3. List everything you own

4. List what you owe

5. Establish a debt repayment schedule for each creditor

6. Consider earning additional income

7. Accumulate no new debt

8. Be content with what you have

9. Do not give up

Having money may not make people happy, but owing money is sure to make them miserable.

—*John Maxwell*

The Value of Going on a Cash Basis as Individuals in a Family

1. It develops individual responsibility and cultivates choice.

2. It provides freedom for differing values within the family.

3. Frustration is reduced and family unity is promoted.

4. It teaches reality: when it's gone, it's gone.

5. It trains children to handle money before they leave home.

6. It meets the husband's need for domestic support and the wife's need for security.

QUESTIONS TO CONSIDER

1. The final step, and perhaps the most important step of getting out of debt is to never _____ _____.

2. Your budget should be:

    A. Written down.

    B. Realistic.

    C. Created in cooperation with your spouse.

    D. All of the above.

True / False

☐ ☐   3. If you want to be free, stay out of debt.

A MARRIAGE TIP

If you borrow money to buy things, you don't own them; they own you.

DROP YOUR DEBT

If you're in debt, make a list of things you can do to reduce or eliminate debt immediately.

_____

_____

_____

_____

_____

_____

Day 5

SUMMING IT UP: GOD'S PLAN FOR YOUR MARRIAGE

Unless the Lord builds the house, they labor in vain who build it.

—

Psalm 127:1-2 NASB

25 TIMELY TIPS FOR COUPLES

We conclude with a collection of tips that summarize some of the most important ideas contained in this text. Read and heed.

1. If you and your spouse want to build a stronger marriage, you can most certainly do it. What's required is a willingness to learn, a willingness to work, a willingness to change, and a willingness to make God your partner.

2. Society stresses the sameness of the sexes, but God's Word recognizes—and celebrates—the differences between men and women.

3. Man was formed from the ground for the ground and is therefore work-oriented. Woman was formed from a man, for a man; she is, therefore, relationally oriented.

4. As a result of original sin, man will have difficulty accomplishing his work. And woman will have difficulty in building relationships and bringing her children to maturity.

5. Marriage is permanent; parenting is temporary.

6. There are certain needs that our mate can meet and certain needs that only God can meet. If we are wise, we learn the difference.

7. If you expect your spouse to meet your deepest personal needs, you'll be disappointed and disillusioned. If you look to God for your deepest needs, you'll be satisfied and blessed.

8. Learn to see yourself as dynamically attached to God, not to your spouse. After all, only God can meet your deepest needs for security and significance.

9. God's Word clearly defines the role of the Christian husband: to love their wives, to lead their wives, and to live with their wives.

10. God intends for men to lead their wives and their families, which means two things: men must take the initiative, and they must be involved.

11. God teaches Christian husbands to treat their wives tenderly, with understanding and discernment. That means husbands should be both gentle and wise.

12. Women need affection, conversation, openness and honesty, financial support, and family commitment.

13. God has clear instructions for Christian wives. They are to help, to nurture, to admire, and to complete their husbands.

14. Spouses must strive to meet their partners' sexual needs or risk serious negative consequences, perhaps even tragic consequences.

15. Wives, your husband needs a best friend and a playmate, and that person should be you.

16. A good homemaker has a plan for managing her home; she honors her husband's homecoming; and she lives within her budget.

17. Wives, your husband needs (and deserves) a world-class cheerleader. You're the one woman God designed to meet that need.

18. Wives, it's your job to respect him and God's job to refine him.

19. Learning to communicate effectively is essential to a healthy marriage. Without clear communication, husbands and wives feel isolated and misunderstood.

20. Because women and men have different motivations and needs, it's inevitable that every couple encounters conflict. Wise couples learn to resolve conflict before their disagreements drive them apart.

21. External anger slept on becomes internal bitterness, so settle it by bed-time.

22. Most of us would say that among our top financial responsibilities are giving and saving for the future. But our checkbooks and credit card statements reveal our true values, which may be very different from our stated priorities.

23. The foundation of your family's financial plan is a written budget that you and your spouse agree upon.

24. Since the borrower is servant to the lender, it's best to live on a cash basis, not on credit.

25. Remember: Marriage is blessed by God, ordained by God, and designed by God to reveal Christ's love for the church. Your marriage has the great potential of making Christ's love visible in this world.

Well, you've made it! This lesson concludes our six-week adventure in building a better marriage. Thanks for your participation and your hard work. We hope that the ideas on these pages will be a blessing to you and your mate. And we pray that God will continue to bless you and yours today, tomorrow, and forever.

Bob and Ann Livesay

MODEL OF HOUSEHOLD BUDGET

Fixed Expenditures (_____/mo.)

Lord _____

House _____

Utilities _____

    Gas _____

    Water _____

    Electricity _____

    Phone _____

    Cable _____

    Newspaper _____

Insurance _____

    Car _____

    Life _____

    Lessons _____

    Car Payment _____

Long-Term Savings (_____)

IRA _____/mo.

Investments _____

Christmas _____

Vacation _____

College _____

Wedding _____

Family Entertainment (_____/mo.)

Short-Term Savings (_____)

Car Repairs _____

Car Registrations _____

House Repairs _____

Furniture Purchases _____

Yard Maintenance _____

(Keep in Cash) _____

Individual Budgets (_____/mo.)

Husband _____

Wife _____

Child _____

Child _____

Child _____

Household Budgets (_____/mo.)

Groceries _____

Seasonal Decorations _____

Household Supplies _____

Personal Budgets (One for each member of the family, age 10 and up)

Lord _____

Savings _____

Clothing _____

Gifts _____

Spending _____

Personal Budget for:

Lord　　　　　_____

Savings　　　　_____

Clothing　　　　_____

Gifts　　　　_____

Spending　　　　_____

Personal Budget for:

Lord　　　　　_____

Savings　　　　_____

Clothing　　　　_____

Gifts　　　　_____

Spending　　　　_____

Personal Budget for:

Lord　　　　　_____

Savings　　　　_____

Clothing　　　　_____

Gifts　　　　_____

Spending　　　　_____

Personal Budget for:

Lord　　　　　_____

Savings　　　　_____

Clothing　　　　_____

Gifts　　　　_____

Spending　　　　_____

BUDGET NOTES:

CHANGES I HAVE NOTICED IN MY RELATIONSHIP WITH MY WIFE